Dining and Driving With Cats

Alice Unplugged

By Pat Patterson

Dining and Driving With Cats – Alice Unplugged
ISBN 978-0-9987922-1-7

Places (P) Eats (E) & Sites (S)

San Miguel de Allende (P)
Mangia's (E)
Mex-USA Border (P)
Austin (P)
Garbo's (E)
Hey Get in Here and Eat (E)
Odeon Cafe (E)
State Capitol (S)
Saint-Germain-des-Pres (P)
Foreign and Domestic (E)
Java Cafe (E)
Texas Tower (S)
Driskill Hotel (S)
Lenoir's (E)
Procope Buci Market (E)
La Tour D'Argent (E)
Paris (P)
Houston (P)
Hollister Grill (E)
Billy's Boudin and Craklin (E)
Billeaud's (E)
Scott, LA (P)
Baton Rouge (P)
Heidelberg Hotel (P)
Ralph and Kacoo's (E)
Dupont Circle, D.C. (P)
Huey P. Long (S)
Red Stick Surprise (S)
New Orleans (P)
Carousel Bar (P, S, E)
Chalmette Battlefield (S)

Butcher's Cochon (E)
Herbsaint (E)
Clancy's (E)
Gautreau's (E)
Cafe du Monde (E)
Buckhead (P)
RT's (E)

The Players

Author
Alice
Lincoln Stevens
CJ Chenier
Franz Mack
Honda Fit
BigLig
Monsieur Billings
Vince Bohrgetti
Danny
Munchie, the Maine Coon
Tuffy, the Fat-Bottomed Girl

<u>Honorable Mention</u>
LeRoy
Evie Mae
OJ, the Perfect

Acknowledgements

To Debbie Alice Patterson who loved me always and never found me wanting I freely dedicate all these words. With these two books, "Dining and Driving with Cats – Alice Unplugged" and the sequel, "Dining and Driving with Cats 2 – Alice Rising" I have attempted to let others see into the heart I gave to Alice.

To my Editor, Bryna Kranzler, award winning author of "The Accidental Anarchist", I could say thank you in every language under the sun and still need to say it one more time. When we started with my words about Alice and her cats I was a story teller. Bryna showed me a destination, guided me on the path and showed me how words can be music to the eye.

To Stewart Williams, artist and designer, your words, "I like things a little more visceral, where there is more of a graphic edge," played out on our cover in a design that gave me courage to say "finished, at last."

To Susan Strecker, award winning author of "The Nowhere Girl", who read every last word and checked my grammar, style and punctuation I can honestly say that without you these manuscripts would still be on my desk.

To every boy and girl, man and woman who gave a splash of water or bite of food to a homeless kitty or adopted a shelter feline, these words about Alice are for you. I hope you enjoy reading them as much as I enjoyed writing them. Do me a favor and take a cat to dinner.

Disclaimers

This is a creative work inspired by an actual car trip that took place over six weeks and almost 2500 miles. The brand of the vehicle was in fact a Honda Fit. The two cats are in fact named Tuffy and Munchy. The restaurants and the meals described are the actual places and menus sampled. We liked them all except for the one in New Orleans which resulted in great stomach distress. The name of that restaurant has been changed.

I would like to thank the real-life members of the BigLig family. The BigLig story is inspired by a real life family whose devotion and love has been an inspiration to literally thousands of families around the USA and probably the world for the past thirty-five years. When you read this chapter you will know why. The actual malady discussed in the chapter and associated medical facts along with the names and identities of the family have been changed to offer anonymity.

I have tried to recreate events, locales and conversations from my memories of them and exactly as they were experienced. The story in Baton Rouge about the "surprise" visit also happened as written with the exception that I couldn't actually locate the "surprise" and resorted to using the photos. The incident with Tuffy in the New Orleans garage was in fact much more frightening than portrayed in the story. It seemed fitting to stick to the lighter side and cat owners should be warned that poinsettias are not the only dangerous substance kitties might ingest. At the F. Scott and Zelda museum in Montgomery I included descriptions from the brochures. We were late for Atlanta and didn't have time to visit all the exhibits. And yes and finally the truth about why Alice refused to say yes to my marriage proposal made at Mr. K's Chinese restaurant is exactly as described in the book. If you really want to know how we resolved it you need to read the sequel – "Dining and Driving with Cats 2 – Alice Rising".

Table of Contents

Foreword – "What the heck?"

This is, above all, a love story — about the love shared between my wife Alice and me, but also our shared love for travel and history, our love of food, and our love for our sweet and wily cats, Munchie and Tuffy. Although these "loves" might seem somewhat disparate, our marriage is stronger for the experiences each of these has brought us.

Alice and I have lived all over the U.S. and in two foreign countries, and have always had animals – cats, dogs, horses, ducks, bunnies, and (yes) mice. For some reason, our travel adventures with cats have been consistently funnier, less predictable, and more interesting than our adventures with other critters.

No cats were harmed during the writing of this book, although we humans have been left with minor physical scars (scratches on our arms and legs) and a few emotional scars from some "near misses". British author Sir Terry Pratchett once said, "In ancient times, cats were treated as gods; they have not forgotten this." We have found this saying to be key to understanding the behavior of cats. Another unidentified person once said, "Dogs have owners. Cats have staff." These two basic principles have governed our relationship and adventures with two cats, which are partially chronicled in this story. And so, we begin . . .

Chapter 1: In the Beginning Was the Plan

"What sort of philosophers are we, who know absolutely nothing about the origin and destiny of cats." Henry David Thoreau

Alice and I were living in the small cathedral town of San Miguel de Allende, high in the foothills of central Mexico. Did I say San Miguel was a small town? Compared to Washington, D.C., our home for the previous 22 years, San Miguel was more like an upscale Latino neighborhood. But it was an unusual neighborhood. No other community its size featured a towering, pink limestone Gothic cathedral with Magic Kingdom castle-like spires pirouetting hundreds of feet above the cobblestone streets and tourist shops below. This distinguishing landmark was known as the Parroquia and it means different things to different people. Mexican shopkeepers apparently believed that the Parroquia conveyed the privilege of being rude and discourteous to the unwary shopper who carried the bizarre notion that if the tiny figurines, hats and shirts were labeled, "Made in China," surely the prices would reflect a substantial bargain. In fact, few, if any of the purchase prices were even displayed on the price tag, and upon querying, the shopkeeper would invariably announce a price that was twice as high as what the half-price sign on the doorway announced. This was a clear case of caveat emptor: let the buyer beware. Prices quoted in the shops around The Parroquia are merely suggestions for where to start bargaining.

In addition to housing a stunning cathedral, the little burg overflowed with stores selling Mexican handicrafts, clothing boutiques, fine arts or jewelry amidst meticulously

1

restored 16th-century Spanish architecture. Almost every Sunday, newspapers in the U.S. ran features praising San Miguel as a romantic destination. Upon reading these stories, the most enthusiastic traveler was ready to sell his worldly goods and move to San Miguel. That was what had happened to us. At the same time, someone visiting San Miguel might be ready to leave after three days.

During our time in San Miguel, my fashion-loving Alice's entire collection of Christian Louboutin, Jimmy Choo, and Stuart Weitzman shoes hung, unscathed and unworn, in specially-ordered canvas shoe racks. Except for two pairs of Stuart Weitzman strappy heels that were being worn by our housekeeper's teenage daughter, the rest of Alice's Jimmy Choo's and Christian Louboutin's were destined to remain unscuffed but not forgotten in the oversized closet. Our little town was not foot friendly. San Miguel's cobblestone streets called for Sketchers, Crocs or for the truly adventurous, Teva sandals. Anything with a hint of fashion or heel could send the most poised women into acrobatic sprawls with only the cobblestones and gravel to soften the landing. The town's nickname, City of Fallen Women, was justly deserved. It was, perhaps, for this reason that the small town had two shops that rented wheelchairs, leg braces and ankle boots while the local hospital featured a 24-hour x-ray and orthopedic clinic.

When not tiptoeing across slippery cobblestones in her clogs, my spouse was happy to pilot her cuatrimoto along the town's notoriously narrow streets. Alice cherished her Yamaha ATV. She loved the bright red color and the soft huffing from the exhaust when she revved the 350cc engine. She insisted that her four-wheeler was the only transportation we needed to enjoy the comforts of our compact town. I had (wisely) agreed with her.

As soon as she had bought it, Alice immediately had her cuatrimoto tricked out to meet her needs. Our handyman had created a two-compartment wire basket that he welded onto the front of the Yamaha. Alice covered the sides of the basket with nylon-screen netting so that the cuatrimoto offered a room with a view for our two kitties, Munchie and Tuffy, for whom it became practically a second home. They looked forward to riding the dusty streets of San Miguel in the luxury baskets of the catmobile as much as Alice enjoyed driving them along the hillside streets.

But after three years in "Margaritaville," Alice began exhibiting signs of 'extremis boredimis'. She was no longer content to spend her hours cruising around town with the kitties, enjoying magnificent azure skies, pastel-colored sunsets, and the endless rounds of cocktail parties that made up our daily life in San Miguel. She was no longer amused by trips to the local grocery where she found the bacon stored on ice behind the car batteries, which were stacked next to raw chickens and ladies' bras. Alice was also quick to remind me that she had endured three years of La Rosa de Guadalupe and other Telenovela soap operas dubbed into Spanglish.

She did not try to hide her restlessness from me. It was clear that she needed a break and expected me to do something about it. Fortunately, the ATV's range limited it to the less than 500-mile distance to the border. The local bus line, Flecha Amarilla (the Yellow Arrow), also did not cross the Mexico-U.S. border, while the bus line that did cross the border – Enlaces Terrestus Nacionales – was not pet friendly. Otherwise Alice, Tuffy and Munchie might have already departed on the midnight coach for Laredo. What I needed to do now was read her mind and act accordingly.

What you don't know about Alice is that she was an expert at putting ideas into my head. She called this type of persuasion 'Kitty Logic' because it was the same way she convinced Tuffy and Munchie to do things like jump into their carriers or take a prescribed medicine. I had spent many years giving myself credit for reading Alice's mind when, in fact, I hadn't been reading her mind at all; I simply

3

responded to the 'travel vibrations' Alice emitted that lodged themselves in my male brain – the same brain that had let me know three weeks earlier that she needed a break from her surroundings. Since Alice's vibrations told me that she was ready to travel – with or without me as long as she had Tuffy and Munchie for company – I knew that I had better do something quickly.

The next Saturday morning, we walked over to Mangia's where we planned to enjoy our favorite breakfast burritos. We sat at our usual table, and I looked Alice in the eye and said that something had been keeping me awake at night. I felt that the time had come to take a long trip. For a moment, I thought the surprised look on Alice's face was legitimate. Had I really surprised her with this news? She grabbed my hand, leaned across the table, and said, "Wonderful" and "Splendid; what a great idea." I was all smiles and "aw shucks" when Alice interrupted my reverie by asking, "What kind of trip?"

She knew immediately that I didn't have a plan. Her telepathic vibrations had only alerted me to the take-a-trip-and-make-Alice-happy need but not to the destination. But Alice already had an answer.

"Why not take a break from Mexico and drive to some of our favorite spots in the U.S.?"

Her suggestion caught me off guard. Were we going to load the Yamaha cuatrimoto with luggage and kitty litter and drive north? Instead of quizzing her, I made a smart decision: I kept my mouth shut and my ears open. Obviously, dear Alice had been planning a trip for some time and had just been waiting for me to have the big idea so she could tell me what we were going to do.

Alice pulled a Hallmark card from her Fendi bag and opened it for me to read. She had collected it from the San Miguel post office box just the prior day and had been keeping it as a surprise. The card was the official birth announcement of our granddaughter who had been born two weeks earlier. Although we had gotten the Vonage call announcing the birth of our new grandbaby, Lela Sidney Anderson, two weeks earlier, the card was an invitation to meet our newest granddaughter, Lela, at our children, Emily and her husband, Matt's, summer home – a beautiful cabin with breath-taking views in Blowing Rock, North Carolina. It was where Emily and Matt went every summer to escape Charleston's sweltering heat. Since getting the call, Alice and I had been 'noodling' over the prospect of making the long trip to Charleston, South Carolina, to touch noses with Lela. Of course, while I had been wrestling with the complications of getting to Charleston and back in one week or less, Alice had silently been weaving together a much longer itinerary. Her hoped-for sojourn from sombrero territory would require weeks, not days.

As I sat mopping up salsa with my burrito, I had to admit that Alice's travel itinerary was an ingenious way of breaking the ennui of Mexico.

Alice Draws a Route

By now, our coffee was cold, and as the waiter refilled our cups, we started to nibble on the sopapillas dusted with powdered sugar and filled with clover honey. Sopapillas, by the way, are not native to San Miguel. Most restaurants served churros with hot chocolate rather than sopapillas with hazelnut coffee. Sopapillas, however, were Mangia's gift to the gringo community. Dunkin' Donuts hazelnut coffee was Alice's gift to the community.

Alice was pleased that I had recovered so quickly from my shock that she had developed a complete travel itinerary so soon after the announcement of my big idea for a trip. I should have guessed that a detailed plan had been percolating behind Alice's emerald-green eyes as soon as she started spending so much time riding the ATV with Munchie

5

and Tuffy. After all, I had been married for most of my life to the smartest person I had ever met.

Spilling a thin layer of sugar on the tabletop, Alice drew our proposed route with her finger as I bit a small hole in the end of my sopapilla and poured more honey inside. Looking at the route, it became clear why the invitation to stopover in Blowing Rock was so important. Alice's plan called for us to cross the Mexican-U.S. border at the Columbia Bridge in Laredo and drive north. Our first stop would be in Austin. Alice filled me in on some Austin dining establishments that had been reviewed on The Food Network.

From Austin, we would take the Gulf Coast route past Houston and stop in some of Alice's favorite cities like Baton Rouge and New Orleans. Knowing how attached I was to Atlanta and the Carolinas, she had added a trek that took us from New Orleans to Atlanta. Alice convinced me with her sugar-map that our trip was optimized for time and distance and to yield maximum pleasure. My lips blew a little smooch across the breakfast plates at the 'optimized for time and distance' remark. I loved it when Alice talked business lingo. She claimed she could not avoid it; business was in her blood.

I enjoyed teasing her about her constant relapse into business mode in everyday conversations with friends. Her success as the owner of a strategic planning company in Washington, D.C., was due in large part to her innate talent for critical thinking. Problem-solving was second nature to her and no problem was too large. I respected her intellect, and was confident that no one was better at planning a complicated trip than Alice. Her 25-year struggle to outmaneuver the capital's bureaucratic process had sharpened her interpersonal and problem-solving skills.

I once asked Alice where she had gotten all her smarts. She took pride in believing that her critical thinking was a genetic gift reserved for descendants of Henry Adams.

6

I wasn't sure if she was referring to the Henry Adams who had written the sophomore required-reading text, *The Education of Henry Adams*, or one of the lesser Brahmins. Having some historical knowledge of John Adams, John Quincy Adams, and Samuel Adams, I had asked Alice to further enlighten me. She had shown me a tattered and frayed, four-inch thick, hardback volume entitled *The Adams Family Chronicles*. After several eye-twitching hours of searching the small print in the genealogy tables, I found a reference to the Henry Adams to whom Alice was related.

It seems that a certain John Willard (JW) Adams was the unlucky grandson of a descendant of Henry Adams of Braintree County, MA. This made 'JW' a cousin to the Presidential dynasty of John and John Quincy Adams, our second and sixth presidents. JW was the youngest son in his family. While his older brother had traveled to London in a luxurious, first-class ocean steamer cabin with his father, the young JW Adams had snuck out of Boston at midnight and had headed west on the Shortline & Erie Railroad. It seemed that JW had had a penchant for backing slow horses. In addition, having borrowed more money than he could repay from some of the North End's most unsavory residents, he slipped out of town and followed Horace Greeley's call to "Go West, Young Man" and sought a new life at the S&E's last rail stop in Platte, Nebraska.

Alice reminded me more than once that her great grandfather, JW Adams, had not survived the hardships of the early Nebraska Territory only to have his progeny stymied by bureaucrats in Washington. In fact (though I always avoided mentioning it), JW had not actually survived any 'hardships'; he had arrived in Nebraska in the first-class coach of a train, not in a covered wagon. Once in Nebraska, he managed to scrape together enough funds to open the first grocery and millinery store for 100 miles. Unlike many of the other pioneers of his day, he always wore custom-made suits and shirts ordered from a favorite tailor in New York.

(Maybe Alice's love of fashion was genetic. It was another question I studiously avoided asking.)

I accepted that her problem-solving and critical-thinking skills were a gift from her Bostonian forebears. She was proud of being descended from a long line of real-life problem solvers, and she took her slightly sullied heritage seriously. Alice lived her life and operated her business on the theory that problems were obstacles in the way of maximizing opportunities. Removing the obstacle was simply a matter of thoroughly defining the problem so that the solution would appear. As she was quick to remind me, "Behind every problem is an undiscovered opportunity."

In this case, the opportunity was an 'escape from Mexico'. Alice, of course, had thought through the opportunity in some detail. I was thrilled at hearing her describe the trip as an exciting U.S. travel adventure that would feed our desire to sample menus in interesting locales where the biggest decision of the day would be something other than red vs. green salsa. We would discover new places and meet new people while anticipating a long-overdue family reunion.

I wondered, however, about the big question that Alice had not mentioned. What would we do about Tuffy and Munchie while we were traveling for eight or ten weeks? As I mulled over this problem in my head, Alice reached over and tapped my coffee cup.

"The kitties will travel with us," she said, while brushing powdered sugar off her blouse.

Using all my will power, I clenched my teeth to prevent my jaw from dropping open and exhaling a very big, "Huh?" Two cats; two months; one vehicle driving day and night. Finally, I couldn't hold it in any longer and my jaw fell open and out it came. "HUH?"

This was not the first time that our feline familiars had been one of Alice's 'problems hiding an opportunity' that was just waiting for a solution. I looked across the table.

8

I could see that Alice was about to explain to me why the solution we had previously employed wouldn't work for this trip.

Three years ago, barely a week after our move to San Miguel de Allende, we had both wanted to satisfy our wanderlust and hit the road to tour the exotic villages, mountains, beaches, and jungles of Mexico. But there was one problem: who would take care of the cats? My brainy mate had come up with a solution that guaranteed our kitties would be safe during our exploration and adventure trip. Why wouldn't the same solution work now?

Lupita Educates Alice

Alice had sensed my reluctance to travel with our furry charges. I harbored serious misgivings over the prospect of traveling for any length of time while herding two cats, or rather, having two cats herd us.

My reluctance was no indication of a desire to stay cocooned in San Miguel; I was ready for an adventure as much as Alice was. In fact, Alice knew the mere taste of travel had always been an allure that had me eager to pack. Since arriving in Mexico, we had enjoyed several trips to the east and the west coasts of this rapidly changing country. Soon after arriving in San Miguel and before selling our U.S.-registered car, we had driven to Oaxaca, and after four days of tequila tasting, returned to San Miguel. During our first in-country, Mexican Thanksgiving, we flew to Cancun and spent five decadent days on the beach at the Ritz-Carlton Cancun as a hurricane destroyed the beach as well as our hotel. During our Puerto Vallarta trip this past winter, we spent almost a week in the little village of Mismaloya with two daughters, two sons-in-law and two grandsons who had joined us for the holidays. On each of these longer trips, Alice had nervously agreed to leave Tuffy and Munchie in the care of our full-time cook and housekeeper, Lupita

9

Munoz. While we were away, Lupita's duties changed from 'housekeeper' to 'cat sitter.'

She would arrive each morning and spend the day in our home watching out for Tuffy and Munchie. Alice trusted Lupita to keep the doors closed at all times and never give either kitty the opportunity to discover the great outdoors. Let it be known, however, that our housekeeper's conversion to 'cat sitter' had required every bit of Alice's skill and persistence to affect the transition.

Before taking the job as housekeeper, Lupita had raised her own family of two sons and a daughter. She and her husband had made the unusual choice to limit their own family size. Lupita had good reason for this un-Mexican behavior. She had been born into one of San Miguel's original 16th Century Mestizo families and had grown up as the oldest of 14 children with the responsibility of caring for her younger brothers and sisters. Lupita knew that the price of a large family was paid by the children. As a result, she and her husband, Ethan, had determined to keep the price low for their own children by limiting their family to the two boys. Only once the boys were men and out on their own had she and Ethan had one more child.

Lupita was now enjoying middle age in the company of a teenage daughter. Part of Alice's persuasion involved letting Lupita's daughter explore with a wardrobe that included Jimmy Choo, Christian Louboutin and Stuart Weitzman shoes (as Alice did not want her wardrobe to go unused and Lupita's daughter was Alice's shoe size). Lupita's daughter, Canella, had the uncanny Mexican skill of being able to walk unassisted in heels, even on cobblestones. In addition to receiving designer shoes and Lafayette blouses and skirts for her daughter, Lupita was being paid an enviable sum to manage a household with two easy-going *Norte Americanos*.

Lupita looked upon her new 'job' as more of a vacation than work as compared with her previous years of

10

enduring the labors of daily life in Mexico. She had taught her eight sisters how to shop, cook and prepare dinner. She had taught her five brothers how to read, write and kick a soccer ball. Even as she struggled with these claims on her time, she had been the first female among her elementary school classmates to complete her mandatory six years and go on to graduate from middle school. She was also the only woman in her neighborhood who could read both English and Spanish.

Lupita had married her high school boyfriend and helped him build a small business repairing electrical appliances and painting *trompe l'oeil* murals. Lupita kept the books and paid the bills while Ethan found the customers and did the work. Between the two of them, they saved enough to buy a small house, raise two boys and pay for them to attend a local college. Throughout all these years of persistent achievement, Lupita had never received a paycheck. She had not even had a 'day off,' and she did not know there was something called a "vacation." Even as she managed the daily affairs of our lives, her family still expected her to cater *quinceañeras* for the younger generation of adolescent girls and prepare a lunch of *tamales* or *enchiladas* for her aging father. She spent her day off raising the funds to obtain hospital and medical care for her mother, siblings and cousins.

After spending two weeks learning to pay our bills, prepare our meals, and oversee the gardener and handyman, Lupita confided to Alice that she felt that cooking, cleaning and paying bills for two *gringos* with a couple of cats was the 'vacation' she had always heard about but never experienced. Getting a weekly salary for not working when the employers were away was almost enough to convince Lupita to return to the church. But she admitted to Alice that her only concern was her lack of experience in *Norte Americano* cat care.

This was the opening Alice needed to facilitate Lupita's transition from 'housekeeper' to 'cat sitter.' Lupita

11

knew that *gringos* liked cats. Lupita herself liked cats, but she had not spent time around ones that lived strictly indoors. In San Miguel, cats lived outdoors. They walked freely around the rooftops and owned the streets at night after the dogs relinquished control. To Lupita, it seemed that *gringos* came from every state of the U.S. to photograph the cats of San Miguel because all the photos she saw on San Miguel kitchen calendars showed black-and-white, or orange-and-gray tabbies jumping, rolling and posing outdoors. To Lupita's thinking, cats living indoors was as strange as humans living outdoors. It was Lupita's lack of exposure to *gringo* cat care that compelled Alice to improve her own Spanish during her first few weeks in San Miguel.

Addressing this issue came down to a Clintonesque moment that still makes me laugh. It all depended on the meaning of *never*. After two weeks of Alice's painful attempt at translating instructions on cat care, Lupita accepted the responsibility and adopted into her understanding the concept that the American word '*never*' meant something completely different than the Mexican '*never*', which seemed to allow for substitution of *seldom* or *hardly ever*. It took two weeks, but Lupita finally understood that Tuffy and Munchie must *never* — not *hardly ever*— be allowed outside for any reason.

The balance of the *gringo* cat-care discussions involved translating additional cat-care terms in Alice's newly adopted language. The definition of "outdoors" included the covered patios on the rooftop and second story, although it did not include the inner-walled patios. After those two weeks, Alice and I were both confident that Lupita could be depended upon to *never, ever* let Tuffy or Munchie roam outdoors.

Additionally, Tuffy and Munchie did not share food or litter boxes; each had her own preference for brand, texture, flavors and location. Alice learned more subtleties of the Spanish language during that two-week period than she had during her two years of University-level Spanish classes.

Lupita was now a trusted kitty protector. I was confident that even our sneaky Maine Coon, Munchie, could not trick her way outdoors with Lupita on watch. Of course, this process made us keenly aware of the risk of losing our kitties when any local besides Lupita was in our home. This rule applied mainly to the dengue fever inspectors, utility bill collectors, the whistling knife sharpener, the *tamales* lady and the other multi-talented and under-worked handymen who cruised our neighborhood daily looking for work. Lupita decided not to let anyone else in our house while we were away except for her daughter, her sons and her husband.

Lupita was a willing student and quickly adapted to Alice's program for caring for our kitties. We were confident she could maintain this strict regimen for a few days or even a week in our absence. She had proved herself more than once when Alice and I left on several exotic forays to visit far-off places within and outside of Mexico. However, we were not comfortable with the thought that Lupita could maintain that level of rigor for eight or ten weeks, which was the minimum length of our upcoming sojourn to the U.S.

Alice decreed that during this trip, there would be no housesitting for the felines. Instead, Tuffy and Munchie would travel with us. Our kitties would be our passengers and just like at home, we would be their servants. Lupita would at last enjoy a real vacation, and Alice would not stress over constantly checking on the kitties' wellbeing.

She could see, however, that I was anxious over the thought of everything that could go wrong. All our combined road skills would be required to manage driving night and day on strange highways, looking for travel sites while avoiding road hazards. Southern drivers and deer crossings would also demand our full attention. Wrangling our tortoise-shell colored fury, Munchie, a bona fide little female terror and our fat-bottomed Tuffy into and out of the car and hotels as we traveled America's highways would test the wild animal skills of a master hunter like Jim Corbett. I could picture Munchie leaping out of an open car window at a toll booth, or Tuffy wandering down to the laundry if a hotel room door was left ajar.

These imagined cat capers were real fears based on prior experience. Tuffy was generally content to stay indoors and only bolted if something scared her. Munchie, however, had more than once demonstrated a capacity for the unexpected. She was quick to leap before thinking. Her lack of fear was a constant test of the nine-lives myth. This past Christmas, she had decided to explore the strings of lights hanging from our third-story balcony. After following me up the stairs to the rooftop patio door several times, she devised a plan unique to her talents as a Maine Coon. Notoriously sneaky, the Maine Coon will appear to be disinterested in her surroundings, all the while taking in every detail and secretly concocting an action plan.

To the typical Maine Coon, the bias is toward acting rather than planning. Munchie was no exception. Unlike Tuffy, she was prepared to act the instant I opened the door to the rooftop patio. She streaked past my feet onto the flat, red-tiled roof and without hesitating to look back, leapt over the wall and into the hanging strands of icicle lights. Only realizing her mistake too late, she found herself hanging three stories above the street, wrapped in the blinking sparklers. Not knowing whether to laugh or cry, I instinctively ran to the parapet wall. Praying she would hang on, I lifted the string of lights with both hands and twisted as many as possible around Munchie's furry body to secure her in a makeshift web while I desperately reeled her back into my arms. But she didn't learn from that experience and continued to follow me up the stairs every day. Without a doubt, she would have repeated the escapade had I not guarded the exit from her continued attempts to escape.

That was not the first time Munchie leapt before she looked. Our former house in the D. C. area had a small Juliette-style balcony upstairs, off the master bedroom. The French doors to that balcony were not allowed to be open unless the kitties were safely on the other side of the bedroom door. One beautiful spring day, Alice opened the balcony door, but before she closed the bedroom door, Munchie had run through the French doors, out to the balcony and jumped. She landed on top of an open umbrella on our deck below. Alice raced downstairs and carefully opened the umbrella. She then climbed onto a chair and reached up to pry Munchie's claws from the canvas to which she clung. Experiences such as these convinced me that the Maine Coons in general, and Munchie in particular, do not buy into 'lessons learned.'

The Great Compromise

Munchie's recent Christmas lights adventure had opened my mind to the obvious. My responsibility for Munchie's and Tuffy's safety fueled my reluctance to undertake this journey with them. Alice sensed as much and as usual was prepared with a solution. She made me a deal I could not refuse. First, I would do the driving and the navigating. The navigation must be planned in advance so that we could concentrate on the tactical aspects of driving and not wander off our planned route. Second, Alice would choose the new vehicle we needed to purchase or rent for the journey. If I could agree to these two points, then Alice would be primarily responsible for the cat-wrangling aspects of our trip. I could not hide my relief. "Sold," I shouted, and we high-fived and hugged under the hallway chandelier. With our roles defined, we agreed to embark in six weeks on July 1. In hindsight, we should have agreed to share the driving and wrangling duties equally throughout the trip, but we did not foresee some of the events to follow.

Once we laid out our itinerary, our trip showed almost 2,800 miles of highway travel across nine Southern states beginning at the Texas border. I took responsibility for calculating driving distances and planning travel stops that coincided with interesting historical sites. Alice took on the heavy lifting. First, she googled traveling with cats and reread current and archived articles in Cat Fancy, Catster and various veterinarian-recommended advice columns. Next, she compiled the first cut of a list of possible dining spots in and around the travel stops I had proposed. In a matter of days, Alice had googled her way halfway across the U.S. Our dining-room table and floor was littered with printouts from Yelp; Thrillist; Zomato; Trip Advisor; OpenTable; Zagat's; NY Times; Top 10; 38 Essential Restaurants, Diners, Drive-ins, & Dives; Where to Dine; 10 Best; 5 Hottest; 10 Worth Knowing; Gayot; and The Food Network. After two weeks of researching, culling the list, debating, stonewalling, and one or two high-fives, we still had not reduced our list to the finalists.

We argued about the purpose of the dining list. Were we looking for the new, the different, the undiscovered? Or were we on a dining audit trail to inspect the most highly recommended spots and see if they lived up to the claims? Was our opinion supposed to outrank the reviews and write-ups that were guiding us in this search? We even considered listing restaurants in each location by genre or category and letting Munchie and Tuffy scratch out the choice. After two weeks of this back and forth and getting no closer to a solution, Alice suggested we turn to another source.

Why not ask our friends for help in selecting our dining destinations? We had many friends in this Mexican town. Making friends was a natural process in San Miguel. Each new arrival soon had an electronic Rolodex file filled with names and phone numbers. Life revolved around cocktails, dinner parties and charity events. These social occasions afforded opportunities to strike up new acquaintances almost every day. Most residents were quick to share their most intimate details with a new friend who may have been a total stranger the day before. San Miguel had grown from a handful of GI-Bill recipients after WWII to a thriving resort location attracting thousands of part-time and full-time expatriate residents with roots in every state of the union. We were friends with many of them and knew how to reach out to hundreds if not thousands of others to help us in our search.

Alice and I decided to mine this knowledge-capital. Soliciting this community for recommendations and opinions on places to dine back in their own hometowns had seemed like a smart idea. We ran one small ad in the local weekly newspaper, *"Atencion,"* which listed our e-mail address. We received 700 responses with almost 2,000 recommendations. Thankfully, many were duplicates. At 62, Austin, Texas, fielded the most non-repetitive recommendations, while Blowing Rock, N.C. garnered fewer than 20. Some responders listed only one or two spots, while others included every taco truck, breakfast joint and hamburger stand they had ever visited. As we culled the responses, the numbers began to reveal some preferences worth pursuing. Our final effort to reduce the list involved watching reruns of the Anthony Bourdain, Andrew Zimmern and Guy Fieri shows on the *Food Channel* that focused on cites on our itinerary. After gathering "way too much information," we managed to compile a final selection. Then the real work began: it was time to make reservations.

In order for Alice to make reservations, she needed to know the date and time we would arrive at each location. We had a list, but we didn't yet have a definite travel schedule. Some dining spots were closed on Sundays, while others were closed on Mondays. I was responsible for computing drive times and distances, taking into account variables such as open and close times and the days or evenings that the restaurants were closed.

I began to whine about my own task. "We would need to stay on a strict driving schedule," was my mantra. I worried aloud about how an Act of God could ruin our whole plan. I must have used the word 'imperative' at least a dozen times.

Alice responded that Mike Tyson had once quipped, "everybody's got a plan till they get hit in the face." We agreed that keeping two kitties healthy and happy might well require an Act of God, and stopping for one sick kitty at a local vet might be Mike's 'hit in the face' factor.

I managed to tweak Alice's 'one last nerve' when I mentioned that we needed a guaranteed reservation at the Niko Bistro in Buckhead, which would be automatically cancelled and no 'rain checks' given in case we failed to show up due to sick cats, flat tires or poor driving. It was one too many whines, and I should have shut up sooner. Alice shot daggers at me and suggested that I stick to the driving and navigating and she would adjust for Acts of God since she probably had a better relationship with Him than I did. All she needed was my travel chart with the stopovers spelled out; she would take care of the rest.

Two days later, she handed me a neatly printed list showing our dining schedule into and through far-off places such as Austin, New Orleans, Atlanta, Nashville, Memphis, Dallas and small towns like Blowing Rock and Banner Elk in between. The list also highlighted the pet-friendly restaurants and put question marks by the others. Alice relied on *OpenTable* to make most of the reservations. In the online form under 'special requests,' Alice had listed our two felines as guests and booked tables for four. She explained that our furry companions would be restrained in cat carriers, and that we would order appropriate treats for them from the day's menu. In truth, Alice was always cautious about offering the kitties anything other than a sniff and a lick of most table foods. Both Munchie and Tuffy were finicky about what they ate, but they enjoyed sniffing new treats. We simply wanted to assure the restaurant staff that we would order abundantly in return for a table for four.

The First Big Surprise

Kickoff time was days away with one big item to go: Alice had not yet chosen our travel machine. I had considered renting a suitable vehicle, but Alice explained why it would be better to buy than to rent. Since we were going to travel in the U.S., we needed something that met all the U.S. safety and pollution requirements. While it was possible, in Mexico, to rent any make of car, they were not configured with the equipment to meet U.S. standards. However, if we bought a vehicle, it would be shipped to us from Texas ready to 'pack and roll.'

Alice had calculated that buying a U.S.-equipped vehicle would also help pay for the cost of our trip. She reminded me that Mexican citizens paid a premium for U.S.-plated vehicles in order to get crash-proof windows, airbags, four-wheel drive and emission controls. We could easily sell our car when we returned.

I was convinced by her logic that the vehicle we bought would be worth more than we paid for it if we resold it on the Mexican market with less than 3,000 miles on the odometer. I also liked the idea of returning to Mexico with my own black tinted-window Suburban. I could just imagine the jealous looks of our cocktail-party friends when they saw me cruise the Town Square in a silver-streaked Ford F-150 platinum, four-door cab truck. The excitement over which vehicle Alice would choose was clear as I watched her flip through all the vehicle brochures.

She was making this choice without getting behind the wheel or more accurately, without getting me behind the wheel. Twice I caught her making notes on the Chevy Suburban, and she kept the Ford brochure with the

19

Expedition and the F-150 next to her bed for several nights running.

Alice's walking buddy, Kathy, convinced her to consider a Japanese brand for reliability and resale in Mexico. Soon, our coffee table was piled high with Honda Ridgeline and Odyssey literature as well as Toyota brochures. When she asked me if I preferred a big SUV to a truck, I made the point that the Ford F-150 came with four doors, a roomy interior, and a weather-tight cargo cover. It would make cat wrangling and luggage handling seem like child's play. I asked her what criteria she was using to make the final choice. 'Flexibility' was her answer. I was pretty certain she would opt for the SUV.

For two days after placing her order and wiring the money, Alice had kept her choice of vehicle a secret, saying, "You deserve a big surprise." One morning, Alice caught a ride with her walking buddy to pick up our new vehicle at the delivery agent's shop. I was left alone on the second-floor patio staring down at the street and trying to guess which passing Suburban (or possibly F-150) was going to stop with Alice in the driver's seat. An hour passed, and the street below was quiet with only the 'dirt man' and his four donkeys in view.

Suddenly, the donkeys sidled over to the broken sidewalks to avoid the black Honda Fit that was spitting dirt as it turned onto our street. It was sharp-looking, with a European-styled hatchback and sunroof. "Perfect for a young couple just starting out," I thought, wondering if a bass fiddle would really fit inside as the television ad claimed.

My eyebrows jerked upwards as the subcompact braked to a stop in front of our house. The driver-side door opened and Alice slipped out from under the wheel. She waved at me to come down. By the time I hit the bottom of the stairs, Alice was entering the front door wearing a big smile.

"It's all ours," she said. Meanwhile, I fell to my knees on the tile floor and begged her to tell me this was a prank and that her friend would be along shortly with the SUV.

"Nope," she said. "This is it, and you'll thank me for it soon enough." At that moment, thanking Alice was not extremely high on my list. We both had a 'Fit'.

It did not seem possible that after all the discussions and all the comparisons that Alice would drive home from the delivery agent's shop in a Honda Fit. She grabbed me by the arm and practically dragged me out to see my big surprise. The price tag said it was Honda's best-selling, most desirable, top of the line Fit. The interior featured full leather on the inside-door panels and seats, both front and rear. She pointed to the paddle shifters protruding from each side of the leather-wrapped steering wheel. She said it was more fun to shift with paddles than her old MGB because there was no clutch. To facilitate easy driving, the fully automatic Fit provided a continuously variable five-speed transmission. She touched a button next to the visor lights and the sunroof slid open. Alice had her iPhone connected to the HDMI outlet, and the Hondalink Navigation pinpointed our Mexican house on the screen in the dash panel. The all-electric power windows and climate control system looked rather ordinary, but the smart key that locked and unlocked the car without taking it from my pocket was unusual. In addition to the reverse-initiated rear-view camera, Alice flipped the right turn signal, and another pin-sized camera in the side mirror displayed everything in the right lane. Alice tapped the console display screen and touched a button labeled Pandora, and the Pandora app on her iPhone began playing a Dixie Chicks tune on the auto's sound system. Two buttons inset into the steering wheel provided hands-free telephone calls, and the Honda came complete with a voice recognition system for connecting, selecting and directing every

21

electronic option. Apparently, Alice had checked off every option on the list when she had ordered the car.

She asked me if it wasn't just the perfect touring car for us. Could I think of anything that would make it more perfect?

Yes, I thought. It would have been more perfect if it had arrived on the back of an F-150 truck.

As Alice handed me the keys, I gritted my teeth and asked, "How am I supposed to load six suitcases, golf clubs, camping equipment, two duffel bags, two backpacks, four pasteboard boxes and 40 pounds of Tidy Cat into that thing, and still find room for two cats, two carriers, a litter box, and a water bowl?"

"You'll figure it out," was all she said – and she was right. That night I immersed myself in 'the ways of the Fit.' By the time I had collapsed the rear seats, creating a small warehouse of room, linked up my phone and Hondalink Navigation, configured Pandora, opened the voice activation console, connected two power supplies and connected the Honda HDMI and three USB ports, I was almost a fan. After flooring the Fit using the paddle shifters to rev the transmission to maximum rpms, I passed the trucks on our local highway and left a couple of BMW r1200 motorcyclists shaking their heads. I was ready to travel. I had agreed that the car decision was Alice's to make. I just had to adjust my mental model of how I would look in the Fit.

America the Delicious

Although our trip started in San Miguel, the bigger adventure would begin at the border: the Mexico-Texas border. We would be leaving our dream house in San Miguel and driving north to enter the U.S. at the Laredo, Texas, crossing. If we cleared the border by 8:00 a.m., we could make it to Austin in time for a late lunch, and kick off our Great Adventure in one of the U.S.'s hottest food towns.

Three years living in Mexico had left us both eager to taste test the changing food scene in the States while on our journey to rediscover some U.S. history.

The first leg of our trip would include two nights in Austin and then moving onto New Orleans by way of Houston. Along the way, we would visit several landmarks that I had selected as much for their unusual circumstances as for their historical significance. We had, individually, visited numerous historical sites throughout the U.S. when we traveled on our jobs. We had made it a point of exploring the local sites our clients had recommended. This trip afforded us the opportunity to visit some new places and revisit others together.

We had two of *Zagat's* highest-rated 'farm-to-table' restaurants reserved in Austin, and I could already taste the bittersweet Sazerac cocktails we would order at Gautreau's in New Orleans. I could smell the smoky sauce I had heard about at Clancy's – a James Carville favorite. I had visions of more farm-to-table delights that we would sample at Aria in Atlanta, and everyone was writing about the Niko Bistro we had booked in Atlanta. We could only imagine what the ambiance might be as we daydreamed about the stuffed peppers at the Antler Bar in Blowing Rock, and the Rock Cornish hens cooked in port wine from Artisanal in Banner Elk. Oh, yes; the road ahead was going to be delicious. But first we had to cross the border.

"Are Those Mexican Cats?"

We reached the Mexico-U.S. border crossing at the Columbia Bridge in Laredo right on schedule. It was half past 8:00 a.m. as we pulled into the right lane on the bridge. Munchie and Tuffy were lounging loose out of their carrier packs. Tuffy was circling the luggage stacked on the back window of the Fit, and Munchie was quietly dozing on the console between the bucket seats, one eye lazily following the trucks passing us on our left. As we crossed over the white lines marking the border, the traffic slowed to a crawl. Most of the cars in front of and behind us just tossed a quick hand wave to the Mexican officers who couldn't seem to care less that we were leaving their lovely country. In front of us, the *Welcome to the USA* sign hung over the inspection stalls that intruded into the lanes entering our native country. Since our Fit was packed with only personal items and we had nothing to declare, I was surprised when the U.S. border guard took our declaration form and waved us over to the holding pen on the right.

On a prior trip at this same crossing, I had been waved over, but I had been driving an auto with Guanajuato tags. The purpose of that stop was to ensure that we had proof of insurance – or maybe to see if any non-U.S. persons had been hiding in the back seat. The border guards generally stop Mexican-plated cars even if the driver says he is a U.S. citizen. But our new Fit had been fitted with Texas Lone Star tags, and the border agent could have asked for ID had he not liked my declaration form. Instead, he sent us to the holding pen.

Alice looked at me with alarm as I squeezed the Fit behind a pickup truck with half a dozen palm trees hanging a good six feet out the open, back-lift gate. Munchie had jumped up onto the dashboard, and I worried about lowering the window more than a hand's width because either cat could spring out the open windows and into traffic lanes.

We sat in silence as the second border guard approached my side. I put on my best grin and lowered the window another inch or two to ask why we had been stopped. He pointed to the rear window. All the windows were tinted, and I was surprised he could see anything.

"Is that a cat?" he asked. I turned around and saw Tuffy standing up with her paws on my headrest. Before I could answer, Munchie jumped over my lap and stood with her paws up on the half-opened window; she started hissing at the agent.

"Two cats?" he asked. I nodded and agreed that we had two and only two cats. He looked at both of them.

"I must see their papers." Of course, in transporting pets, it is not unusual to be required to provide proof of vaccinations and results of recent tests for parasites and other medical issues. We did not forget the papers. What we did forget was that we might be stopped and asked for them. In fact, three days before we left, Alice had escorted both Munchie and Tuffy to our Mexican vet and gotten all the shots and paperwork completed in both English and Spanish.

The agent could see the relieved grins on our faces as I assured him that we had the required papers – but where? I glanced at Alice, then toward the back. The Fit was jammed with boxes and luggage, and I had no idea where we had stowed the documents. Alice shrugged; she told the agent that we had the documents somewhere in the car but it would take some hunting to find them. Now we were in a jam. Both cats were loose. We couldn't just open the doors and step out to unpack a lot of boxes and luggage. The agent leaned in close as I started trying to capture the kitties while Alice started digging in her Louis Vuitton monogram handbag looking for the papers. Both cats knew something was up, and they darted away from us as I shouted to the agent that it would be necessary to get the cats into their carriers before we could unload and start looking. This seemed a grim way to start our journey and would have been even more painful if the border guard had not sensed our frustration.

He leaned toward the crack in the window and put both hands and fingers on the glass as he asked us a yes or no question.

"Are those two Mexican cats or U.S. cats?"

I looked at Alice and we both answered together, "U.S. cats, of course!"

The border agent touched the brim of his hat, stepped back from the car, and waved us on. God bless America! I revved up the Fit and we spun into traffic laughing so hard that we almost had to pull over to get control.

Chapter 2: First Stop: Austin

"Cities, like cats, will reveal themselves at night." Rupert Brooke, English poet

In spite of our stop at the border, we remained on schedule. The highway to Austin offered a fairly easy drive. We had a full tank of gas, and at 39.8 miles to the gallon, we passed San Antonio and didn't even need fill up until we got to San Marcos, about half an hour south of Austin. We had planned to be in downtown between 1:00 p.m. and 2:00 p.m., and we were going to make it.

Our first 'Dining with Cats' meal would be lunch in Austin, Texas, at the 'pop-up truck scene.' Our favorite food blog, SeriousEats.com, crowned Austin the Pop-Up Food Truck Capital of the U.S. We were set with our choices for lunch, but for dinner allowed ourselves to be influenced by something Alice had spotted on the Zagat web site. Zagat had recognized Austin as the best city for farm-to-table small restaurant dining. Alice chose Lenoir, and I added my vote for Foreign and Domestic.

With so many reviews on pop-up food trucks, it was no easier to make our lunch choice than our dinner dining spots. As we had dined so often on street tacos, carnitas and asada in Mexico, we decided against the Tex-Mex, Brazilian BBQ, and Zarzuela de Mariscos pop-ups, as well as all the Jerk Chicken, Burrito, and Texas Chili pop-ups. Our first dining experience on the "Dining and Driving with Cats" journey would be enjoyed at the pop-up food truck just off South Lamar Street called Garbo's. That was where we were heading in a Honda Fit jammed with cats, people and luggage. We were on our way to thrill our taste buds with what some critics were calling the most exciting, tantalizing taste ever offered in a pop-up food truck. We were making our way to 'lobster-roll heaven.'

The Austin pop-up truck scene has become a featured attraction for most tourists and concert attendees. In fact, some of Austin's most notable dining spots started off as pop-ups, many of which had 'popped up' near a concert venue. Today the scene is really different. Not only do the trucks have published locations around Austin, but they also have a gathering spot near South Lamar Street where a dozen or more trucks can be found in one spot. This is truly "Pop Up Nirvana".

Pop-Up Nirvana at Garbo's

With both kitties circling around inside the Fit, I was concerned about driving straight to our lunch spot rather than stopping at our hotel and unloading first. But Munchie was already clamoring for food, and there was no one who loved lobster more than Munchie. A Fancy Feast Medley cat since adoption, Munchie turned up her nose at most other offerings. She made an exception for lobster. But she didn't eat lobster; she typically just licked it. So on we drove, not wanting our kitty to miss such an enjoyable treat. Our target, Garbo's, was just ahead.

We arrived at 1:30 p.m. The downtown skyline jutted up like the Rockies. I knew from the map that the Colorado River was somewhere down below the skyline, and the view from our vantage point was great. There was just one problem: there was no place to park. We still had the windows up and air conditioning on, but the pop-up lot was filled with trucks. The only place to park was across the street in the lot behind Zax's American Fare. I wondered if they would mind. I pulled into Zax, and the valet leaned toward my barely open window. I said we had come from Mexico, and our cat had her heart set on a Lobster Roll from Garbo's. Could we please park in the lot for 30 minutes and take our cat to the pop-up truck? The young lady looked me

28

in the eye and said, "We believe that *keeping Austin weird* is everyone's responsibility. Of course, you can park, but 30 minutes, tops."

Alice decided we should take both kitties in their carriers. First, we needed to wrangle them into the carriers, which is never an easy task except in the mornings. Any other time of day, they each seem to sprout ten legs and paws that we have to contend with. After pleading with both felines to hop into their carriers, we managed to secure them. Alice and I each hung a carrier over our shoulder and headed for the trucks.

The lot ahead of us was filled with taco trucks; gyro trucks and vegan donut, crepe and cone trucks. Every truck had a substantial line of people waiting for a preferred treat. When we found Garbo's, there were only about five or six people ahead of us. We recognized the menu immediately. We had perused the items many times online. When our turn came, I ordered one Maine Lobster Roll and one Connecticut Lobster Roll. That's when I realized the reason for the short line. Top dollar at the gyro and taco truck was $4.99. Garbo's prices started at $22.50 but were worth every penny.

We found seats with about six other people at one of the picnic-style tables in the pop-up truck lot. Everyone wanted to see what was in our packs. We unzipped the top portals and both Tuffy and Munchie lifted their heads, and gave the crowd those quizzical looks that only cats can pull off. Munchie immediately let out her hunger whine. I waved the Maine Lobster Roll by her nose, and she tried to grab it with her paw. The Maine Lobster Roll is served with drawn butter, while the Connecticut Lobster Roll is paired with a homemade mayonnaise. Munchie smelled the butter and began shaking her head with desire. I decided to treat Munchie to something besides the sweet butter on the Maine Lobster Roll. Everyone laughed as I pulled off bits of Connecticut Lobster Roll with the most delicious creamy and tangy mayonnaise I had ever tasted. Munchie quickly licked the small piece I had offered. The little taste seemed to satisfy her, and she settled back in her carrier to bathe while we finished our lunch. Tuffy had already decided it was nap time. She was worn out from her border-crossing adventure.

I was into my second bite of the Connecticut Lobster Roll before Alice had her first real taste of Garbo's. Alice thought the lobster chunks were as creamy as butter. Each bite was melt-in-your-mouth delicious. The texture was firm but easily broke down on the tongue, and I tasted a faint hint of the ocean in the back of my mouth. Garbo's uses brioche buns with a slot cut in the top of the bun – perfect for the thick chunks of lobster. Like a sponge, the brioche sucked up the butter and the mayonnaise, and magically collapsed around the lobster chunks, forming a mouth-watering combination. Each roll came with a small side of sweet pickles and tasty chips with a picante spice that was a perfect match. Try as we might to linger over these succulent rolls, each bite ignited an irresistible urge to take one more. And just like that, the rolls were gone.

Everything we had read about Garbo's was true and even better. Although our time in Austin was short, we made a pact to try one of the other pop-ups before leaving town. We had no idea that we wouldn't have to return to the Lamar pop-up scene for our next food truck experience.

Texas Tower as History

Lunch was already a distant memory by the time we got checked into our pet-friendly hotel, unzipped the carriers, settled both kitties in for a two-day stay and unloaded our two tons of travel baggage. Alice thought it best to let the kitties stay in the hotel room and get accustomed to new quarters while we toured. We have found that pet-friendly hotels are experienced at avoiding any pet confrontations. We left Tuffy and Munchie with proper food and water. It was still early in the afternoon, and our dinner was not till eight so we had time for our first historic site visit. Our hotel was on the central east side of Austin, and as we left the hotel parking lot, we could almost see our destination. We were headed for the University of Texas (UT) – home of the Longhorns. Our first 'catless' stop was the Texas Tower on the University Campus.

Standing upright in the middle of the UT Downtown campus, the Tower is 304-feet tall with a parapet-protected observation deck around the top. By modern building standards, it is not tall, but it is more than just a tower and more than just an icon to academic pursuits. The Tower is more like a 27-story, block-wide office building with a tower protruding from the center. The University President's office is on the fourth floor. We had reserved the Tour at the Tower, which has been closed to the public for over 40 years since the serial massacre of August, 1966, in which Charles Whitman, a lone rifleman, killed 30 people and wounded 32 more. It had only recently reopened.

In the early hours of that August morning, the gunman murdered his own mother and killed his young wife. He left a suicide note next to his wife's lifeless form saying that he was sorry for what he had done and requested that his brain be autopsied to find out what was wrong with him. He believed something beyond his control was making him do terrible things.

After killing his own family, he jumped in his truck with a high-powered rifle and hundreds of rounds of ammunition and headed to the UT campus. Whitman approached the unguarded entry of the main Tower building, and without being noticed, entered the elevator and rode to the inside foyer one level below the open parapet. Three visitors were already on the elevator, and Whitman shot and killed them. Once on the walkabout, hidden by the parapet walls, he aimed his scope-mounted rifle at pedestrians strolling aimlessly around the nearby streets and along the campus walkways. His position almost 400 feet above the

31

ground completely muffled the sound of the rifle as people began to fall to the ground. Three Austin policemen and one civilian bravely entered the Tower and headed to the observation deck. Two of the policemen broke through Whitman's homemade barricade and fatally shot him.

More than 30 years after the Texas Tower tragedy, a new generation experienced the Columbine tragedy that many think is the first instance of mass killings of innocents, but that had started at the Tower. Investigators first believed that this irrational act of violence had occurred with no reason but the autopsy Whitman had requested in his suicide note proved different. Charles Whitman, engineering student, and ex-marine sniper, had a brain tumor.

There was much more to the Tower than the tragic Whitman history. The artwork and architecture were worth the trip, but it was getting late and we needed to head back to the 'cat hotel' and check on our pals. We also had to get ready for dinner at Austin's top rated farm-to-table dining room known as Foreign and Domestic.

When we opened the door to our hotel room, Munchie and Tuffy were both nestled on the bed showing no signs of regaining consciousness after falling into a kitty food coma after we had left. They seemed quite happy, and we were ready for our next adventure.

Pigs Ears, and Bacon Root Beer Floats

From the outside, Foreign and Domestic is anything but imposing. Its one-story cinderblock building might once have been an auto repair garage. It is also not easy to find, but our Hondalink saved us from missing the place entirely. We had made early reservations to ensure we had the pick of the menu, and also because we knew some other diners might not be thrilled to see us feeding F&D samples to our cats.

We had received permission to bring the felines to dinner as long as they remained in their carriers and out of sight. "Out of sight" at F&D was a little difficult as the place is rather small. Not including counter seating, it accommodates 40 diners, tops. But it was cozy and chic. The counter was terrific for "chef watching" as it opened onto the sparse but efficient kitchen. The booths along the walls were inviting, and the tables in the center were arranged to give every guest the space they needed to enjoy the flavors of the day. The wait staff was attentive and immediately sold us on trying one or two of their specialty beverages while examining the menu.

I chose the *Cyclist* and Alice ordered the *Champagne Punch*. The *Cyclist* was beautifully herbed and iced, but I had forgotten how 'gingery' a ginger beer laced cocktail can be. Alice, who is a longtime lover of the ginger spice in a Kentucky Mule tasted it and said it was delicious. I had also forgotten that I was driving and decided to settle on the house lemonade for the balance of my beverage choices.

The server offered help in selecting from the various offerings. It was a challenge; should we start with the *Black Pepper Gruyere Popovers* that we had read so much about? Maybe the *Crispy Pig's Face* (yes, pig's face prepared crispy), an infrequent menu offering, or should we order something lighter, like the *Apple and Mushrooms with the Baby Kale, Olive, Anchovy and Miso*. So much to try and so little time. We decided to start with a combination of *Fried Pigs Ears with Shishito Peppers* and one order of the *Black Pepper and Gruyere Popovers*.

So far, there were no problems with the kitties. They seemed content to sit by our feet and make gentle purring sounds. The popovers were served first, but as soon as these buttery delights hit the table, everything changed. Tuffy got one whiff of the gruyere and suddenly 20 pairs of eyes started looking for the source of the high-pitched meow she had let out. Tuffy did not ordinarily eat people food, but she loved cheese, especially gruyere. Her love for cheese evolved from trips to our vet who gave the kitties a treat of *Easy Cheese* from a can whenever administering shots.

We had experienced Tuffy's continued passion for cheese at a fondue party Alice had hosted, and should have known she would carry on loudly demanding cheese until she was satisfied. There was nothing to do but acquiesce. Alice ripped off a small piece of the popover, and after gently blowing away the heat, proceeded to stuff it into the cat pack where Tuffy began to loudly smack her furry little cat lips. Seizing the moment ahead of the next dish's arrival, I ripped off a piece of the popover and took a bite. The word "scrumptious" is inadequate. The popover's rich savoryness combined with the pepper made it worthy of an entrée. I was especially glad we had come early. Alice and I are familiar enough with popovers to know they are best served immediately from the oven, and ours had been born barely a minute earlier. They were so flavorful and texturally comforting with the gruyere adding a soft, cheesy taste. Tuffy was content and so were we.

When our next dish arrived, we had an inkling of why this spot called Foreign and Domestic was so high on everyone's list of favorites. *The Food Network* had called this place a "culinary wedding of flavors". After one bite of the *Fried Pig's Ears and Shishito Peppers*, I was high-fiving Alice regarding our great choice for our first dinner in the U.S.

I had always thought of pig's ears as a Southern delicacy, but I suppose it has gone global. These pig's ears were perfectly cut so that when they were fried, the gelatinous portions remained semi-rigid, and combined perfectly with the bits of pork. Match this crunchy goodness in your mouth with Shishito peppers – a classic served with many sushi and sashimi dishes – and you get a tasting experience equal to none. I was sure we had already reached the pinnacle of dining heaven for our six-week trip.

Our F&D entrees arrived together. We had decided on the *Fried Chicken Biscuit* and the *Halibut Plancha*. We both cut into the *Fried Chicken Biscuit* and decided to conduct simultaneous taste tests. Alice's face stretched into a big grin as the first bite crumbled on her lips. I did the same. This is one place where the words 'best red-eye anywhere' need to be inscribed on the front door post. Anyone who has eaten the *Red-Eye Sausage Cream Gravy* splashed over the *Fried Chicken Biscuit* will never be satisfied again after tasting it at Foreign and Domestic.

Next, we moved to the *Halibut Plancha*. The lemon comfit spread under the fish was subtle, but the entire dish radiated joy in my mouth. I saw from Alice's eyes that this dish puzzled her. To my taste, it was the equal of the halibut that any restaurant had ever prepared. The fish was perfectly done, and the crusty edges were almost sweet. It was the asparagus that had tickled Alice's mouth differently than it did mine. The dish had been prepared with chicken skin and trout roe scattered on top. I had cut the fish careful to scoop up the sliced strawberries layered with the asparagus and chicken skin. The flavor combo was a real treat to my tongue, but Alice thought the asparagus had slightly trampled the sweetness. This is nothing new since we often had differences of opinion on our food, but I thought the asparagus set off the buttery taste of the fish.

Our debate was totally wasted on Tuffy who, until this moment, had not stirred after receiving her cheesy treat. It was clear, however, that the aroma of halibut had wafted close to her nose as she was starting to try to pull apart the top of the pack handle to reach the fish. I cut off a piece that had cooled and slipped it into her carrier. Unlike the delicate Munchie who always prefers to lick her food into digestible form, Tuffy was a bit of a gobbler. The entire piece was gone in two bites and she was asking for more. She gladly accepted what I offered and nosily finished the next bite.

Alice rolled her eyes, a comment on Tuffy's less-than-ladylike manners.

As for the evening's overall success, we got what we had come for. We came for tastes and flavors prepared with everyday restaurant provisions. We wanted a farm-to-table experience with creative dishes that would provide us with lasting memories, and we got both at F&D. We knew there were many other wonderful places to dine in Austin but we were glad to have started here.

Cats Hate Leftovers

Our second day was to be our last in Austin before heading to New Orleans. We had a full day to explore and eat, with dinner reservations at 7:00 p.m. We awoke excited to get rolling. Tuffy and Munchie had spent the night, as usual, bedded down on top of Alice and me. Munchie was the lighter of the duo, but having her spend the entire night weighing down the small of our backs could bring twinges in the morning.

Tuffy was subtler. Starting her evening at the foot of the bed, she would wait till the human slumber was underway, at which point she would begin her move. Slinking ever so slowly along my legs, she would slide her way up to my back. Tuffy's weight provided a furnace of heat, and I usually spent my nights gently moving her off me and re-curling into my nest, only to rinse and repeat the whole process several more times until morning.

At first light, the high-pitched yowling started. It was time for IAMS and Fancy Feast. Both critters demanded instant gratification in the morning. Nothing but top speed would suffice, and the bowls had better be overflowing.

While Alice cranked open the Fancy Feast for Munchie, I heaped an overflowing helping of dry IAMS Adult out to feed the furnace that was Tuffy. In addition to their specific brand preferences, both Munchie and Tuffy required that their dry IAMS and moist Fancy Feast cat food had to be freshly opened. That meant we couldn't fill their bowls in the evening and then sleep late while the felines dined without us. Munchie needed to hear the can being opened and sniff the wafting aroma before tasting to make sure it was fresh. Tuffy needed to see the dry IAMS pour from the bag. It didn't matter if I had dumped the dry leftovers from the night before back into the bag as long as she saw me dipping into the IAMS bag for the morning morsels. Once feeding was over, we were free to begin our day, and both kitties settled in for the first of several daily naps.

The Road to Java

Our morning would start with a page from the *Austin Chronicle* playbook. We had read about the *Best 100 Eats* and had taken special notice of the breakfast hits. The Magnolia Grill was rated top notch, but it was also on the south side where we would be enjoying our evening meal, so we voted to head north toward Cafe Java. We drove about ten minutes on the expressway before pulling onto Lamar and keeping our eyes peeled for the strip shopping center. Flanked by a Discount Gas and Dairy and Otoki's Pure Dry Cleaners, Cafe Java looked welcoming with a small overhang shading the wide sidewalk from the sun. A couple of antique wooden chairs sat out front with small round cafe tables for diners intrepid enough to sit amidst the diesel and gas fumes from Discount Gas. But once inside, Java exceeded our hopes. The place was a classic small-town diner. The walls were lined with booths, and the center of the floor held tables big enough for four with plenty of room to walk around them. On the far side was a dining bar complete with high-back stools with footrests for lazy legs.

When we arrived at about 9:45 a.m., we saw a few people standing outside, which we took to be a good sign. Alice always says that you can tell how good a restaurant is by the number of people waiting for it to open. We pushed open the door and faced a standup placard informing us to *take any empty seat of your choice*. We spotted a booth that was clearing out and got a quick wink from the waitress telling us to move in. It is important to note that we did not bring the kitties with us. Breakfast is our only break from our servant duties, and we take it seriously.

It is also important to note that Cafe Java is what breakfast dining is all about. The service is top-shelf. There must be five or six wait staff, and each server acts as though all patrons are their personal customers. Smiles, hellos, chats and 'please enjoy' were all standard. I could tell this place loved customers, and it was clear that the customers loved it back. As scribbled notes arrived in the kitchen, the cooks shouted out the short order code name going onto the griddle. In the dining area, the servers carried two pots of coffee – gourmet regular and decaf – that were refilled at no charge.

The two chalkboards at the front and the big one hanging on the wall in back announced the day's specials: *Migas, Miga Grande, Flap Jacks and Pearls, The Scrambler, 2x2x1, Wall Eyes,* and *Fat Bob's Demise.* In addition to these chalkboards, there was the menu that included *Mama T's Fatback Burger, Mountain Dan's Daybreak, Cook's Eggs* and *Belly Strips.* Of course, *Huevo Rancheros* and *Huevos (your way),* along with pancakes, waffles, and *Java Red-Eye Gravy* were also offered. I took the *Scrambler,* avoiding as many of the high-carb side dishes as possible. Alice went light with the *2x2x1.*

We heard our orders being shouted in the kitchen according to our booth name, which we noticed was marked 'Pink.' By the time our server brought the second coffee pot, we heard the unmistakable shout of "Pink Up." Our waitress turned around and, as smooth as any running back in the NFL, handed off both coffee pots to her colleague as she deftly scooped up the Pink order of plates from the serving bar. Without hesitation, she spun our way, both arms stacked with plates and saucers, and bent to table height to slide our breakfast dishes in front of us.

"Anything else?" she asked. "Just say 'Pink' and I'll be right over." She smiled and left us to enjoy the feast.

Our choices were perfect. Alice's *2x2x1* included two eggs over easy, two pancakes perfectly poured, and one strip of *Dan's Mountain Bacon* that was crisp and wide enough for two. My *Scrambler* consisted of a heaping plate of Grade AAA, supersized eggs, scrambled medium soft and layered with my choices of red and green pepper strips, tomato slices and provolone cheese bits melted to perfection. All this was covered in a *Hatch Green Chili* sauce. We split our plates to share the bounty of Cafe Java.

We longed to grab a local paper and sip more coffee, but needed to get back to the kitties and prepare for our second historical site visit. As we walked to the register, I realized that no ticket or check had appeared.

The 'registermeister' smiled and said, "You 'Pink?'" I nodded, and he rang up the order with his right hand while filling two take-away cups of coffee with his left. My iPhone flashed Apple Pay as the attendant rang up the payment for breakfast and said, "On the house," and passed me the no charge cups of steaming hot coffee. "Go be weird," he called as we pushed out the door.

Cat Scares, Capitols, and Hotels

We headed back to our hotel to ensure that the kitties were copasetic with our day's agenda. We had a busy afternoon planned and hadn't made up our minds about whether to take the felines with us. When we arrived at the hotel, we had a bit of a shock. Even though the hotel was pet friendly, we always worried about the attendants who entered the room. Guests are instructed to keep the pets in carriers, cages or other confinements when away from the room so as to ensure that attendants can provide housekeeping services without any pet problems. We were more conservative. Alice kept a Do Not Disturb sign on the door handle at all times, and told the desk not to service the room until we called. This way, we could leave the kitties to explore and play freely while we were out. During our past adventures, this method always worked.

But today when we returned, the Do Not Disturb sign was missing from our door. Someone had entered and no doubt spotted Tuffy and Munchie roaming about the room.

The kitties would not have been frightened by a stranger, but we worried that a housekeeper might inadvertently let the kitties escape. These were house cats; neither had ever been into the great outdoors, and both were certain to meet an uncaring world devoid of caretakers or servants if they escaped. They knew nothing of cars, buses, unfriendly dogs, little boys or lawn mowers. They wouldn't last long on the outside.

Our hearts skipped as we opened the door. We expected the worst – an empty room. The last thing we expected to see was Munchie preening on the TV stand, and Tuffy napping on the bed. We were so relieved to see them we almost missed the note. On the bedside table was a single sheet of paper with a penciled scrawl that read, *"Sorry to enter but one cat was making loud noise. Black gato was stuck in TV stand. I fixed room and cats very nice. Everything OK, Maria."*

"What the heck?" I turned to Alice; she was already at the TV that stood on a bureau with a hinged door at the front. Alice pushed on the door and it swung in rather than out. We instantly saw the problem. Our hot furnace (and slightly rotund) baby Tuffy had been overcome with curiosity and pushed against the small door. She must have suddenly found herself trapped inside when the door swung shut behind her. The housekeeper must have heard the yowling and crying and come in to the room to check. We were so relieved! We gave Maria silent high-fives and promised to have a drink in her name at dinner. I also resolved to leave a bigger than usual tip 'for Maria.' After this scare, we decided that taking the kitties with us on our next historic site visit was not a good idea. We gave them each a lot of attention until they settled in for yet another nap. We then double locked the door and put out another Do Not Disturb sign.

It's Always Bigger in Texas: The State Capitol

One might question our choice of the Texas State Capitol as one of America's most important historical sites. After all, there are 50 state capitols, and the populations of each state must think that theirs is the most important. A reasonable belief, but easily parried once the truth about the State Capitol building in Austin is known. This was the largest State Capitol in the entire U.S. of A. It covered thousands of square feet above- and below-ground. There are 392 rooms with an astronomical number of windows and doors. The only capitol building that is larger is the U.S. Capitol in Washington D.C., but even so, the Texas State Capitol building is fifteen feet taller. They say that everything is bigger in Texas, and this was no exception.

The building, itself, sits on the highest point in the city so the views are extraordinary. A city ordinance controls the height of all Austin city buildings to prevent blocking the view of the Texas State Capitol.

When we arrived at the Capitol complex, a tour group had just left. One of the Texas state troopers noticed our disappointment and asked us if we wanted him to show us a few highlights. We jumped at the chance to receive a more personalized tour, and after snapping a few photos with our personal trooper tour guide, he filled us in on a few historical facts.

First, anyone who has visited Washington, D.C., will be familiar with the Renaissance revival architectural style of the Texas Capitol. It is awesome at its site in downtown Austin and is one of the most popular picture postcards in the state. Construction on the Capitol didn't begin until the 1880s. It was designed to be big – really big – and that meant expensive. Picking up the tab for such an enterprise was a Texas-sized problem, and it took a Texas-sized idea to come up with a way to pay for it.

It would take seven years to build, and employ over 1000 men just to quarry the red sunset granite from Marble Falls, Texas. In 1882, the cost was over $3.7 million (almost $400 million in today's dollars). Our guide asked if we could guess who had this sort of funds available in 1882. The answer was "nobody." That kind of money was not available to anyone, anywhere and especially not to spend on building a not-for-profit state capitol.

But the one thing that was plentiful in Texas, which the contractor would accept in lieu of cash, was land. In exchange for constructing the Capitol, the contractor received 3-million acres of prime, Texas Panhandle real estate. It was the largest private land deal ever consummated at that time and was how the XIT Ranch came into being. One interesting tidbit about the XIT Ranch: besides being the largest privately owned land ranch in the U.S., XIT Ranch also had some strict rules when it began operating. The trooper laughed as he told us that no weapons were allowed to be carried for either defense or offense while on XIT land. Apparently, the cattle rustlers loved this rule. Eventually, the rustlers, along with falling cattle prices, drove the XIT Ranch out of business.

Our guide spent almost an hour showing us various spaces inside the Capitol, but the real treat was when he accompanied us outside to see some of the historical monuments that pepper the Capitol grounds. Outside is the *Great Walk* and is the main entry to the Capitol. The area is park-like, and covers about 20 acres. It is covered in a black-and-white, diamond-patterned pavement, shaded by trees, and flanked by twenty monuments. The trooper pointed out several, including the Heroes of the Alamo, Volunteer Firemen, Confederate Soldiers, and the Texas must-see monument: Terry's Texas Rangers.

It was still early when we said goodbye to our trooper guide. He asked about our next stop. Since there was plenty of daylight left, he suggested that we top off our historical site tour with a walk to the Driskill Hotel. That was how we discovered one of the most amazing places in Austin, Texas.

Next Stop: Driskill

The walk to the Driskill Hotel was only about twenty minutes from the Capitol. Following our trooper guide's directions, we spotted the building from a distance. But the height, alone, was not sufficient to catch our attention. The Driskill occupies the entire corner of Sixth and Brazos Streets, and stands only four stories tall. What makes this a magnificent-looking structure is that it looks like it is made of gingerbread. We had seen a similar style in western cities such as Denver and San Francisco.

When we entered, there were only a few guests milling about, and we asked the concierge if she had any pamphlets or history on the building. As soon as I told her that we had only been in town for one day from Mexico, and were visiting for the first time, she insisted on providing us with a personal tour of the hotel.

The Driskill was built at the same time as the State Capitol – around 1886. The hotel is small by today's standards, with only 60 rooms, and 12 corner rooms with gingerbread balconies. These were the very first hotel rooms in the west to have attached baths. Today, all the rooms have been modernized and include en suite, spa-like bathrooms.

The concierge led us outside so we could view the three sides of the building from the corner of Sixth Street. Each side had its own arched entryway. The concierge pointed above the entries, and we could make out the carved busts of Mr. Driskill and his two sons, Bud and Tobe.

The hotel is located at the very entrance to the music and bar district of Austin and is near The Chugging Monkey and Maggie Mae. In a way, it seemed out of character to have such an elegant, Romanesque-style hotel located on one of the wildest, party-music streets in America.

44

Standing in the lobby on the ground floor, our eyes were drawn to the spectacular rotunda, which reminded us of the Brown Palace Hotel in Denver. The Driskill was built with an open design to facilitate airflow and keep the structure cool during hot Austin summers. Originally, the rotunda extended up to the fourth floor, and culminated in a spectacular domed skylight. Today, only the rotunda remains after the building was renovated to include air conditioning. The Driskill is still the home of each new Texas Governor's Inaugural Ball – a tradition that dates back to 1887.

We had a quick tour of the upstairs lounge and bar where we stopped for a Texas Toddy and enjoyed hearing the rest of the hotel's colorful history from Sam, the bartender. Sam asked if we recognized the lavish dining room. It was a replica of the one in the St. Regis hotel in Manhattan which was featured in the Sandra Bullock movie, *Miss Congeniality*.

Even more interesting was the LBJ connection. This was where LBJ first laid eyes on Claudia Taylor, the future Lady Bird and the hotel they returned to on every trip back to Austin on the way to their ranch in Texas Hill Country. LBJ watched the results of his own successful 1964 Presidential election from the oversized Driskill Presidential Suite and addressed his supporters that night from the Driskill Ballroom.

We thanked Sam for his hospitality and decided to head back to check on the kitties, discuss our plans with them and get ready for the evening's next big adventure which was to take place on the south side of Austin's Colorado River, about ten minutes from the Driskill.

Monte Cristos in Paris

We headed back to our car with nothing in our stomachs except the Texas Toddy we had shared back at the bar with Sam. It was long past lunchtime, and we had big dinner plans at 8:00 p.m. Could we afford to pass up an opportunity for one more trip to Pop-Up Nirvana? While we talked it over, we turned a corner and saw 'it': The Hey! You Gonna Eat or What? pop-up food truck was parked 50 feet in front of us. One look at Alice and I knew this was the right stop to make. Back in the spring, when we were deciding where to eat in Austin, we had settled on Garbo's for all the right reasons, but there had also been one that Alice could not let go of – the pop-up named Hey! You Gonna Eat or What?

I didn't have to ask what we were going to order. I knew it wouldn't be the *Spicy Reuben* with hickory-smoked brisket, spicy slaw and pepper jack cheese, coated in habanero aioli. Nor would we be sampling the *Texas Mesquite Turkey* smoked in mesquite, layered on a ciabatta baguette with pepper jack cheese and fried green tomatoes and smothered with homemade jalapeño jelly. Neither of these was going to win out over Alice's favorite, the *Monte Cristo* sandwich. Alice had dined on *Monte Cristos* and the equally tasty *Croque Madams* around the world.

We had made our first trip to Paris in the late 1980s when we spent 31 days in the City of Lights during the Christmas and New Year's season. Our room was a third-floor walkup with a tiny Juliet balcony window, French doors and a private tub and shower cleverly built into the back of the closet. At an exchange rate of eight to one, the Franc was undervalued. We had pooled our meager funds to go during the low season, and the exchange rate made it possible to stretch our funds as far as possible.

Monsieur Billings had welcomed us at the front door of our hotel on Rue Jacob and he could tell from our disheveled appearance that the then ongoing Paris taxi and subway strike had not been kind to us. We had been forced to drag our two duffle bag suitcases along the sidewalks from the Gare du Nord in a 35-degree misting rain, across the Seine, past Boulevard Saint-Michel, past the French Quarter and down Rue Buci two blocks behind the Church of Saint-Germain-des-Pres.

But we were young and resilient, and had arrived at last. Monsieur Billings, sympathetic to our condition, helped us to our room with our bags. It was half past four in the afternoon, and the mist was turning to snow. Darkness was pouring down the wintry streets of Paris. We were exhausted, cold, wet and hungry. We stood in the doorway of what was soon to be the very spot we would remember as the place we fell in love for the second time. Without even asking, Monsieur Billings set down our bags, clapped his hands and said, "I have just the plan for you."

He turned and pulled back the closet door and inside was the white marbled backsplash behind a deep-walled tub. A filigreed-glass window above it looked out into the darkening alley down below the hotel. As he turned on the tap, he informed us that hot water was only available in the mornings from 6:00 a.m. to 9:00 a.m. and evenings from 4:00 p.m. to 8:00 p.m. We were to get out of our wet clothes, hang them over the tiny radiator, enjoy a hot bath and after recuperating, meet Monsieur Billings downstairs for further instructions.

Looking back on our first hours in Paris, I can only conclude that if every visitor's first experience with French hospitality had been like ours with Monsieur Billings, the French service industry would deserve a superb reputation.

While we enjoyed the hot bath, Alice and I had thrown our plans out the window and decided to enjoy our first night in Paris following Monsieur Billings suggestions – whatever they may be. It was half past six when we approached our hotelier at the front desk. He was smiling broadly at our happier expressions. He extended his hand with a folded piece of paper with a line drawing; it was a simple map of the area. Monsieur Billings pointed out the "X" mark for the Cafe Relais Odeon on Saint-Germain-des-Pres and then pressed his business card into my open palm.

47

"Just give the waiter the card," he said, "and let him take care of it all." It was not even a ten-minute walk to Café Relais Odeon, and the shimmering lights along the street reflecting in the wet pavement started to wake us up. Alice turned to me when she heard my stomach rumbling, and we both laughed at our situation but were happy to be near the sharp aroma of gruyere cheese.

We handed Monsieur Billings' card to the waiter, who glanced at it and led us to a small table by the front window. We sat without a menu or even a chalkboard to guide us as our waiter neatly uncorked a bottle of white wine labeled *Bouchard Pere et Fils Bourgogne*, filled two glasses to the brim and sat them in front of us. We both took a sip as the waiter placed the bottle on the table and said in softly accented English that our "di-*neh*" would arrive momentarily. This was so unexpected that we just repeated "*Merci Beaucoup*" over and over as the waiter drifted out of sight. Before we could discuss what this was about, the moment of truth arrived. Our waiter returned holding a chintz-fringed tray above his head. As he lowered it, we saw two covered chafing dishes alongside the largest basket of french fries I had ever seen at a restaurant. In one crisp jerk of his hands and a shouted *Voila!* he removed the covers. There on the white china plates were two smoking hot *Odeon Monte Cristo* sandwiches.

You always remember your first one, and Alice has never forgotten hers. We were so hungry, and the *Monte Cristos* were so delicious. Each was piled high with the sweetest, smoked Iberico ham, sliced paper thin, layered with razor-thin slices of pinion-roasted turkey, stacked and laced with melted gruyere, all enveloped in battered and toasted brioche that melted on our tongues. This was the ultimate *Monte Cristo*.

Now we were standing in line at Hey! Ya Gonna Eat or What? and all I said to Alice was, "Monsieur Billings would be happy."

48

What a smile Alice can put on when I say just the right thing. I wanted to relive those memories with her, but our turn was next at the food truck. We ordered one Monte Cristo and split it. After all, we had another dinner adventure barely three hours away.

Was the Hey! Ya Gonna Eat or What? offering equal to the Odeon Cafe's *Monte Cristo*? My guess is that Monsieur Billings would be the first to take the food truck's *Shiner Bock Beer-Battered Sandwich with Pit-smoked Ham and Mesquite-smoked Turkey, Cheddar and Provolone Cheese accompanied with a Homemade Cherry and Fig Jelly* right into the Relais Odeon Cafe and say, "Start making them like this …" That was one delicious sandwich.

Finding Heaven in a Little Dish at Lenoir

It was time to head to the hotel, check in with the kitties, and get ready for tonight's adventure. Our dining experience at Foreign and Domestic had equaled our hopes. As we enjoyed our epicurean delights last night, it did not dawn on us that something even better was in store for us at Lenoir.

Alice and I had read everything we could find on this little jewel of a dining establishment. We had seen photos of the food and pictures of the interior and exterior. We had even read comments on various forums seeking opinions. Everyone seemed to have a favorite dish at Lenoir. Alice and I knew it would be hard to choose. In our excitement, we forgot that not all the dishes were available every day. Lenoir is a farm-to-table specialty house and very seasonal, as well. Alice and I had not considered that the dishes that caught our eyes in a review might not be available tonight.

It didn't matter. The Lenoir menu listed items that could only have been created by someone whose mind was not normal. Of course, we were in Austin and 'not normal' was sort of considered normal. But first we had to find the place.

It was on First Street, south of the river. You could look back up the street at the new high-rise profile of downtown Austin that made a striking contrast to the one-story architecture that covered the south side of town. Lenoir is on the street, and there is parking – for about five cars. We were fortunate, because the Honda Fit could squeeze in almost anywhere (Thank you Alice!).

The restaurant is housed in what looks to be three separate, one-story buildings connected in a zigzag arrangement. This made for a nice interior patio area with springtime benches and tables set up for those wishing to brave mosquitoes, heat and stray doggies. We had reservations that included one cat named Tuffy. Considering the creative nature of the Lenoir menu, Alice decided that Tuffy was the best choice to bring as she would try anything. Munchie, on the other hand, was pretty hooked on Fancy Feast and some occasional lobster.

With a new lightweight, Sleepypod cat carrier hooked over my shoulder, I grabbed Alice by the hand and we headed for the entry. Lenoir challenges the new diner with a more-than-slightly-hidden entry door. Its clever placement offers just a hint of the unexpected that you are about to experience in Lenoir.

We had arranged for seats at the bar, and as we entered, our host for the evening extended his hand and said, "Welcome." Carrying Tuffy in a Sleepypod was a sure giveaway of our identity, and our host led us to our seats. Lenoir is a chic place. It is even smaller, in terms of seating, than Foreign and Domestic, accommodating perhaps 30 diners at one time. The narrow windows on two sides were covered with a gauzy and billowy fabric that let in afternoon sunlight but provided a cool shade, as well. The center of the room is lined with picnic-style seating on a hand-polished, white birch dining table with matching pull-out benches along the sides. But the most eye-catching features were the light fixtures above the long, narrow picnic table. Hanging in ragged symmetry at different elevations were about 35 beautiful captain's lanterns. The glass fronts and sides were attached with sparkling strips of brass that reflected the incandescent candle flames burning within. The tables along the two walls were almost standing-height bar tables, and each had two hand-cut, white wooden stools with foot rungs and carved backs for guest comfort. The tabletops were polished, white-streaked birch wood. The white birch continued at the bar where we sat. The combination of white birch, gauzy window treatments, and the slightly shadowy interior highlighted by the brass-and-glass captains' lanterns lent Lenoir a sense of the shared intimacy of a private dinner for two – or three, in our case.

The female bartender leaned across the polished wood bar and flicked open a tan beverage card featuring Lenoir's signature cocktails. She fished a longer menu card from her server's apron and presented us with a wine and beer list. So far, so good. Turning away for a few seconds, she pulled from beneath the bar a handwritten tablet with all the day's menu offerings. The Lenoir menu is always *prix fixe* with choices listed under *Field, Land* and *Sea*. Desserts are listed under *Dream*. The small plates' arrangement and fixed price makes it easy for two people to choose six of anything to share at one moderate price. The two of us had a six-plate combination to provide us with a taster's choice. I liked this freedom to choose. I liked Lenoir.

Our bartender offered to help us with our decisions. Clearly, she was familiar with the tastes and ingredients of all that Lenoir had to offer. She was, in fact, a work of art herself. Alice and I couldn't stop staring at her tattoos. We had been in Austin for less than two days but had already accepted the fact that permanent body artwork was an expected condition, not an exception. Our checkout person at the Whole Foods grocery store where we had stopped for bottled water had purple hair pulled back on one side with the other side shaved revealing a shooting star trailing a small line of smiley faces. The male desk attendant at our hotel sported a boa constrictor tattoo around his neck that seemed to open its mouth each time the attendant spoke.

But our bartender was exceptional, and did not mind extending her arms so we could study her more closely. From the tips of her fingers, delicate vines of blue and red with intricately carved leaves curved and swerved around her forearms. The leaves were each numbered, and referenced a chapter and verse from the King James Bible. Alice didn't notice this, and I didn't point it out as I wasn't prepared to have a Baptist experience with a bartender in Austin. After the personalized tour of the 'tattooed lady,' we collected the cocktail menus and placed our order.

Bring a Cat to Dinner

I ordered the Texas Old Fashioned, and Alice decided to try the Kentucky Mule. Tuffy was content to purr quietly in her carrier, which the bartender allowed us to place on an empty chair. Tuffy seemed content to lounge in her Sleepypod while gazing at us from her eye-level perch. It only took a moment before she emitted a little yelp, seeking attention. I stuck my hand in to pet her. After a few sips of our drinks, we decided it would be okay to let Tuffy sit on Alice's lap – as long as she remained in the Sleepypod. The bartender agreed. But I forgot that the top of her carrier was a bit open. This would turn out to be a big mistake in bar etiquette. While I began reading off the list of the night's dining possibilities, Alice began stroking Tuffy through the small opening in the top of her carrier, which only expanded the flap further.

Lenoir is a small-plates, farm-to-table establishment that prides itself on using locally grown ingredients. We knew the menu changed daily so we had prepared by reading customer reviews that covered lots of options. I was not disappointed that the *Seared Antelope Heart* was unavailable. I was hoping to see the *Rice Crusted Drum*, as it would have been interesting to compare it to the Foreign and Domestic *Halibut Plancha*. The drum was unavailable, but two other seafood items were offered. As our bar neighbors received their orders, it became clear that Lenoir was into foam. Both appetizers our neighbors ordered were beautifully plated and lightly foamed. One was the *Papadum with Heirloom Tomatoes, Chilies and Yogurt*. It was impossible to match the second plate, which wafted an aromatic smell our way, with anything I saw on the menu so I asked our neighbors about it. They were quick to say it was their favorite, and they came to Lenoir at least once a week. The dish was *a Popcorn Carbonara with Sweet Onion Noodles, Smoked Mushrooms and Pecorino*. It was large enough to be a two-way starter or a main.

Alice was interested in the carbonara dish and so was Tuffy. The pecorino-cheese aroma was too much for the little feline, and without any notice she pushed through the expanded enclosure on Alice's lap. With one bound, she landed her full 16 pounds on the bar just inches from our neighbor's popcorn carbonara. Alice lunged across me but was too late. Tuffy slid across the smooth bar top with her back claws scratching for a hold. That was followed by the sound of a cat shoulder smacking into the plate of popcorn carbonara, which sailed off the edge of the bar and into our neighbor's lap. So much for bringing a cat to dinner.

What ensued next was a mix of shock, outrage, apology, more outrage, abject apology and finally laughter. Tuffy, stunned by her moment of freedom, leapt behind the bar. I was grabbing at the spilled carbonara and stuffing bar napkins into our neighbor's outstretched hands. The bartender tried to scoop up the mess while Alice held Tuffy whose sleek fur was dripping with cream sauce. As I kept apologizing, one of the diners began laughing. Her partner, however, was paralyzed in horror as creamy morsels of still-smoking carbonara dripped down her little black dress.

While the other Lenoir patrons were leaning into our predicament, the bartender raised both hands and shouted, "Touchdown! The cat scores six!" Just like that, our experience turned into an 'Austin Weird Adventure.' The offended diner regained her composure and began laughing loudly and uproariously. In fact, everyone burst into laughter just looking at the scene. At that moment, Alice wrangled Tuffy back into the Sleepypod. Like an NFL player who had actually scored the winning touchdown, Tuffy sat back on her haunches and started preening as Alice checked the carrier for any future potential escape routes.

The rest of the evening at Lenoir's proceeded without further interruption. The bartender handled everything. The two diners were reseated with fresh glasses of wine, their dinners paid for by a cat named Tuffy. The three of us, at the bartender's suggestion, moved to the outdoor patio that was beginning to fill with the night's diners. We decided to keep Tuffy incognito while we tested the Lenoir menu.

I was tempted by the *Quail Stuffed with Octopus* but decided to try the *Porgy Ceviche* and one of the meat entrees. I selected the *Red Curry Goat* that was fixed in a heavily creamed *pastilla sope* in *escabeche*. Our dinners in Mexico often included tacos topped with the pickled carrots that made up the Mexican *escabeche*. The Lenoir version was similar, but a little overshadowed by the red curry. I loved the goat curry. What surprised me was that the curry had been mixed as an Indian red base when I had been expecting the Asian version. It was a delight! After practically inhaling the sweet *Porgy Ceviche*, the lingering taste was re-excited by the red curry. *Ceviche* is also a big item in Mexico, and the Lenoir preparation, using the chili salt, and floating the *ceviche* in summer melon soup, was better than any *ceviche* south of the border. The *Coconut Avocado Sorbet* was a special touch, and just another example of how these small-plate restaurants in Austin were setting the flavor bar high.

Alice had decided on the night's specialty in the *Field* category, which was described as *Sunchoke Soup with Beets*. She had spent several years working in Manhattan, and one of her favorite places to dine was the original Russian Tea Room near Carnegie Hall. Alice had developed a love for *Chicken Kiev* and *borscht*. Seeing the soup offering, it made sense that we should sample the beet soup in memory of her days in New York.

We also ordered the *Miso Loaf* that came with a kimchee spread. Without doubt, this proved to be one of the best combinations of flavors we had had during our entire journey, but it would not be recognized in the Russian Tea Room. Tasting the soup with the *Miso Loaf* was like discovering hot biscuits with butter and strawberry jam for the first time. I hoped the Lenoir chef would begin offering these two items together as a single tasting experience.

Next came the *Tandoori Quail*. Alice and I have always appreciated the flavors of India. The tandoori cooking style is traditionally done using covered clay pots in hot ovens. Meats and fish cooked in the tandoori style typically have a slight infusion of the Indian flavors but are not as saturated as the curries and kormas that are steeped in garam masala. The Lenoir *Tandoori Quail* is exceptional in that the moist, but roasted, skin almost bubbles off the meat. Its base of blackberry soy sauce meant that every bite of the tender bird was immersed in a softly sweet taste of soy.

The bird is accompanied with a corn puree and roasted okra that transform this dish from a taster's choice to a hearty meal. I was glad we didn't have to choose our favorite from that night because we would have started one of our heated arguments. I would just say if I am ever back in town, I will have some beets and quail. We split the *Toasted Coconut Pudding*, paid our bill, collected our softly-snoring Tuffy and drove to the hotel wondering if Austinites know how lucky they are to live in a place where 'weird' is a true state of art.

Back at the hotel, Munchie greeted us with a yawn and a stretch. She sniffed Tuffy extensively as if the night's adventure could be recreated through its scent. Both kitties took long baths that slightly shook our bed as we fell asleep.

Chapter 3: BigLig and the Secret Recipe

"Women and cats will do as they please, and men and dogs should relax and get used to the idea." Robert A. Heinlein

Morning came early. Tuffy was dancing with her full weight on my stomach, trying to get me to wake up and open the IAMS bag. Munchie was hunched on Alice's still-supine back, busily bathing every inch of her Maine Coon fur. We had planned our 'get up and get ready' routine to eliminate the possibility of forgetting to pack things like paper towels, extra water, Cold-Eeze gummies, and the plethora of cat paraphernalia. Our hotels were mostly self-service, so every stop was a chance to demonstrate my portage skills. I loaded our eclectic mix of bags, boxes, and pillows, along with the litter boxes and kitty toys, which required the skills of an Ed Sullivan plate juggler and Cirque de Soleil Chinese contortionist. Balancing everything on the hotel's industrial-strength luggage cart while pushing it down hallways, into elevators and across curbs to the car was soon to become routine. It should be noted that the 180-count Bounty roll of paper towels will actually reach the length of a hotel hallway if it tumbles from a hotel trolley stacked with litter boxes.

Alice's job was convincing two wary and perceptive felines that it was time to burrow into their carriers and enjoy the zipped-in luxury of being carried to their favorite playroom – the Honda Fit. I have watched her pull this feat off many times, but to this day cannot duplicate her skill in advanced cat herding. Alice places each carrier fully unzipped on opposite sides of the room. This 'revelation of carriers,' as we call it, sends each kitty scurrying to whatever hiding spot it has already mapped out. This is usually under the bed but might be in the window alcove behind the curtains or curled behind the TV in the hotel armoire. Once they have hidden, Alice chooses a chair or bedside and sits down quietly with a book or magazine open and begins to flip through the pages. One by one, each kitty appears from its clandestine nook, slowly ambles over to Alice, and begins to rub against her legs. Jealous of her devotion to the book, each cat attempts to get her attention. Without a wasted motion, Alice leans over and scoops up Tuffy and tucks her into the nearest carrier that is quickly closed and zipped. The curious Munchie follows like a shadow, staying close to Alice's feet while intently studying every detail of her cat mate's capture and detention. Once Tuffy is carefully tucked away, it is a simple matter of scooping up Munchie and repeating the scene.

As simple as this method sounds, I have tried it numerous times, and I could read *War and Peace* before either of those two rogues would reveal themselves to me for capture. Alice pulls it off every time and in less than two minutes can have both kitties safely ensconced and loaded into the Fit while I still struggle to find space for the last backpack.

A Change of Plans: Houston Detour

As we pulled out of the hotel parking lot, Alice plugged my new iPhone into the Honda Fit's USB charger. It immediately chirped to inform us of a new text message. Alice scanned the message while I slowly pulled into the Austin traffic. The message had arrived the night before while the phone was off saving valuable airtime.

It was from BigLig. "CUN (see you in) Houston – the hotel is open," was all the text message said.

Alice and I looked at each other with amused grins. This was a response to an e-mail I had sent almost six weeks ago as we were preparing for our trip. Our friend, BigLig, was a fourth-generation Bostonian who, two years earlier, at the urging of his oldest son and daughter, moved himself, his spouse, his special-needs son and his mother and father from Boston to new quarters in Houston, Texas. During the past two years, BigLig and his wife had visited us once in Mexico, and we visited them in Houston, but mostly we stayed in touch via e-mail and an occasional text from my new iPhone. At the outset of our planned 'Great Adventure,' I emailed BigLig and told him that our itinerary could afford a short layover in Houston, Texas. He responded with his usual "LOL" and "anytime, anytime, we will be here." There had been no other communication since then.

We concluded that BigLig had other things on his mind than housing us for a night, so we had taken his silence as a polite refusal. How wrong we were. In our note, we mentioned that our travel plans would put us in Houston on July 4th, and BigLig's message was his way of saying he would be awaiting our arrival anytime on that date. Today was that date. We had planned to drive from Austin to New Orleans to enjoy the Mississippi fireworks from the balcony of the Monteleone Hotel. Instead, we would be spending the 4th in Houston with BigLig and his ever-expanding family.

As we were already underway, I decided to call BigLig using the car's voice-activated controls. The car asked for the name or number. Alice and I laughed at the interlocution of an English sounding operator whose robotic responses actually worked. The phone on the other end rang through to voicemail. I told BigLig that we would be in by 1:00 or 2:00 p.m., and reminded him that we had traveling companions so he could let us know if anyone was allergic to cats. We could always stay at the nearby Embassy Suites, which we knew was pet friendly. No one objected to our furry companions, and by 2:00 p.m., we pulled off Memorial Drive into BigLig's housing enclave, wondering what was next.

A Little Boy and BigLig

Thirty-five years had passed since I had met BigLig. It had been in Boston at the Old Castle Conference Center where a computer exhibit and conference was underway. I was leading a small group of computer programmers in a dismal effort to explain to the audience how, one day, every computer would be able to search for and find any data, any news, any statistic, any fact that had ever been recorded and stored digitally. Attempting to put this capability and its value into meaningful terms a full ten years before the existence of the World Wide Web and the Internet was the most dismal aspect of the show. I couldn't explain the future, and the audience couldn't get it – except for one person: BigLig.

He got bigger as he approached me. Dressed in an expensive-looking suit, custom tailored to his 350-pound frame, he stood my height at over six feet but had me by almost 200 pounds. He shook my hand as I read his name-tag: 'Jerry Liggit.' He was listed as a private investor. BigLig was visiting the high-tech conference looking for investment opportunities. This encounter began a 35-year-long friendship.

As we pulled into BigLig's driveway, Alice and I were surprised to see the garage door opening and a clean-shaven, lanky fellow in a sleeveless Texas A&M sweatshirt step out and wave at us. He appeared too old to be BigLig's oldest son, Jeff, yet there was some similarity. Our mouths dropped open as this person reached our car door. It was BigLig himself. No longer 350 pounds, he was a svelte middleweight topping 189 at most.

The three of us got everything out of the car, including the kitties, and before long we were sitting in BigLig's home-office suite hearing the story of a miracle diet. BigLig had wrestled as a heavyweight in college at Johns Hopkins when he weighed 305. The years, and perhaps the good living, had added to those pounds, and at 350-plus, BigLig realized he had to make some changes. Curiously, the catalyst for change had come from an unusual source. According to BigLig, it had been Daniel, or Danny as we knew him, who had delivered the message. "If Danny delivered a message, it was a miracle," I thought.

Danny was Jerry Liggit's youngest son who could not write, speak, see, nor voluntarily move any part of his body. Daniel was born about the time BigLig and I met at the computer conference. From the date of his birth until the night of his fourth birthday, Danny was a bona fide, athletic child phenomenon. Every bit as muscled as his big brother, Jeff, and as coordinated as his big sister, Joan, little Danny had one additional trait that distinguished him from the rest of his athletic family: Danny was quick. By his second birthday, the only thing the little speed demon couldn't do was snatch a fly out of midair. Before he could walk, at only ten months old, Danny swam the length of BigLig's backyard pool, kicking his feet while popping up to breathe. When other kids were learning how to stand on two feet, Danny was climbing onto the backyard trampoline and doing handstand flips. On his third birthday, he sat on his new BMX bike, and with one shove from BigLig, he was soon doing wheelies in the dust along the curb.

On the night of his fourth birthday party, Danny developed a runny nose. His mother, Carol, took his temperature; at 4:00 a.m. it was over 103 degrees. At 5:00 a.m., Danny was admitted to Children's Hospital. At 9:00 a.m., the doctor gave a diagnosis Danny's parents could not bear. Danny was suffering from bacterial spinal meningitis. His life was in peril from the deadly bacteria, which was much more difficult to treat than the viral type.

BigLig and Carol were in shock as the doctor described the deadly nature of Haemophilus influenza type b. The bacterium was already attacking Danny's gray matter, and the most powerful antibiotics available were not slowing the relentless inflammation of Danny's cerebellum. Carol listened. She would never forget the depth of painful loss this cruel meningitis bacterium effected upon her family. Danny was born ten years before his mom stunned the American medical community with her relentless effort to have the "Hib vaccine" developed and introduced as part of the routine childhood immunization schedule. Thousands of parents would one day thank Danny's mom for saving their children from the ruthless destruction being inflicted on the little boy who would never thrill his family with his amazing ability, again. Danny's brother and sister could only stand by helplessly as the bacteria drove the fever that continued to rage inside their desperately ill little brother's body.

Darkness was spilling into the intensive care unit on the third day as BigLig watched the attending physician supervise attachment of the ventilator Danny required for breathing. On the fifth day, the doctor found Carol lying alongside her little boy who could no longer hear his mother's breath, look into her eyes or squeeze her fingers. "He is not coming back" were the only words Carol heard as the doctor went into a detailed explanation of the extensive neural damage Danny had suffered. Most cases, the doctor explained, end in death when the disease attacks the brain's autonomic nerve center controlling the heartbeat and blood pressure, but in Danny's case, vancomycin arrested the meningitis before it had extinguished the tiny spark that still glowed in Danny. His life expectancy was now in BigLig and Carol's hands.

Only the hoarse whoosh and low hum of the ventilator broke the deep silence that enveloped the room as Jeff and Joan took hold of their brother's tiny fingers. BigLig, the doctor and Carol jumped as the little boy's right fist uncurled and a tiny elfin thumb stuck straight up in the air.

The physicians and nurses attending Danny Liggit never expected the boy to leave the hospital. The doctor assured BigLig that the child's thumb movement was involuntary and not related to his mother's pleas or his brother and sister's touch. He emphasized that the child would never breathe on his own or have control of his bodily functions. BigLig and Carol would not hear any of it. Over the next few weeks, the Liggits rearranged their house, hired experienced caregivers, purchased medical equipment and fought with insurance companies so that Danny could go home.

Now, after 30 years, BigLig and Carol, with frequent help from Jeff and Joan, worked with a team of nursing professionals who provided around the clock care for a little boy who defied the odds. Sometimes at night, when his sister Joan reads him stories about the Velveteen Rabbit, or his big brother, Jeff, sits and reads the Red Sox box scores to him, the little boy inside would raise the tiny thumb. His eyes were always open, and his breath came in long, steady heaves. Even Carol claimed that sometimes she caught the glimpse of a smile on Danny's lips. After 30 years, Danny was still her little boy.

Only Danny wasn't so little. Unable to move, and confined to a bed and motorized chair, the little boy never missed a meal by tube. Weighing almost 120 pounds, Danny was BigLig's responsibility to move from bed to chair to pool and even to the car for routine and emergency hospital visits. Last winter, BigLig had finally met his match. What had been a lightweight task when he was in his thirties had now become a major tactical challenge as he approached Medicare age. BigLig's size restricted his ability to care for his son. He had to make a change.

Enter the Italian

Having spent most of his life in Boston, BigLig had made many acquaintances that he had nurtured into lifelong friendships, such as the one we enjoyed. One of these friends was a transplanted Italian named Vincenzo Bohrgetti. Long known as Boston's most flamboyant, exotic, imported auto dealer, Vincenzo, or "Vince," was an accomplished Renaissance scholar. As scion of the owner of one of Milan's most distinguished fashion brands, Vincenzo was expected to follow in his father's footsteps and continue the competitive battle with Gucci and Fendi. Vincenzo had other plans. He had excelled as a student, loved cars and cooking, and was an accomplished linguist and Renaissance literature aficionado. Vincenzo decided to make it on his own, left home without a dime, and arrived in Boston looking for work as a translator.

Two weeks after landing at Logan International, Vince met BigLig at a North End Italian restaurant where Vince earned ten cents a word translating Crespi's Italian Diner's recipes into English. BigLig was sitting at a nearby table, wining and dining a prospect for his bond arbitrage business. Apparently, Vincenzo overheard the lunch conversation between BigLig and the client regarding the client's futile search for a mechanic who could work on his Lamborghini. Vincenzo took the opportunity to offer his services. Once Vincenzo explained that his father's home garage had sheltered Lamborghinis, Ferraris, Maseratis, Alfa Romeos, and one or two stray Bugattis, the future was no longer in question. In short order, BigLig had raised the capital to put the one-time Dante scholar into Boston's first exotic sports car showroom. Forty years later, Vince was repaying the favor.

Selling exotic autos had not kept Vincenzo from his pursuit of knowledge or the perfect cannoli. His reputation among his friends and family as a showman was eclipsed only by his skill in the kitchen. Vincenzo had pioneered something among his acquaintances called the 'Eating Mediterranean Method.' It was all about eating healthy while enjoying fine dining but without gaining weight. Vince repaid his debt to BigLig by volunteering not only to help him in his weight loss plan but also teaching BigLig how to cook and eat the Mediterranean way for healthy living.

The only way to accomplish this involved moving from Boston to Houston to live at Jerry Liggit's home during the teaching process. For ten months during the past year, Vincenzo Bohrgetti had lived with the Liggits and overseen BigLig's transformation from size XXXL to L. Listening to this story would not have been half as profound if we had not been staring at proof that BigLig was no longer "Big."

The Secret Recipe of How to Make a Child Smile

We arrived at BigLig's at lunchtime. Before sitting down to hear the story of BigLig's transformation, we had unloaded a few traveling items, including the two felines. BigLig's two-story home was a veritable amusement park for Munchie and Tuffy. Alice carefully closed the doors to various rooms and closets to avoid any 'hide and seek' games that the kitties might decide to play. They enjoyed discovering every nook and corner upstairs and downstairs as we watched BigLig whip together an Italian salad deluxe.

The recipe called for a very large stainless steel or aluminum mixing bowl; very large. This was one of those IKEA types used for mixing four dozen eggs or, in this case, mixing two heads of iceberg lettuce and a large bag of romaine. Before dumping the chopped rabbit food into the bowl, we watched a professional act of virgin olive oil treatment. Using only two tablespoons of oil, BigLig was able, with a few swishes and swipes, to coat the entire inside of the metal bowl. Lettuce was then tossed two-handed in the bowl until each cut piece was thinly coated with oil, as if by magic. Next came the off-the-shelf, white albacore tuna packed in water, not oil. Once this protein was stirred into the mix, lunch would be ready.

By now we knew that BigLig was spending the holiday alone. The week of July 4th week was when his wife

Carol took her annual trip home to Bangor, Maine. Those annual trips were the chance to rekindle the "ties that bind" that kept Carol's family (the Aldens of Mayflower Compact fame) close in spirit to one another regardless of where they lived during the rest of the year. In this case, the trip included BigLig's extended family of son, daughter and four grandkids that had also made the trip to Maine to spend July 4th at Grandma Alden's Bangor estate. But someone had to remain behind to look after the miracle boy, Danny, and that duty had fallen on BigLig.

Not that my friend minded remaining behind. His relationship with Grandma Alden tilted more toward diplomatic recognition than the son-in-law peonage the Alden name was expected to engender. The Mayflower Society connection and governor's estate had not deterred BigLig from pursuing the woman of his dreams during his post-collegiate days. Perhaps the sheer preposterousness of a super big Jew from Bean Town expecting to win the hand of the fair maiden descended from the Plymouth Rock founder, himself, had stunned the future in-laws into a defenseless posture against his persistent pursuit. Marriage had quelled the Aldens' initial prejudice. The birth of BigLig and Carol's first child invoked a change of heart in Grandma Alden that only a grandchild can produce. No one loved Joan and Jeff more than Mrs. Alden who doted on the grandkids and the great grandkids, and once again adored the wayward daughter, Carol, who, in marrying Jerry, had in every respect vastly improved the Alden gene pool.

BigLig was still mixing the tuna and salad greens when Alice began wondering why the kitties were taking so much time to find us downstairs, particularly since the house smelled like tuna. It was time for a cat search. What we found brought us to tears. After looking in every corner and every closet up and down, the three of us met together downstairs but empty handed. The only sounds in the house were the low vibration and hum coming from Danny's room

66

where the standby ventilating equipment was running. BigLig pushed open the double-wide French doors that separated Danny's living and sleeping space from the rest of the downstairs. The humming was coming from Danny. He was lying flat on his back in the hospital bed, propped up on inflatable supports. The near comatose man-child was slowly nodding his head. His eyes were open and staring upward as he continued to emit a soft, chesty hum. We watched silently as Munchie and Tuffy perched hawk-like on the inflatable bed. Each kitty was sitting on one of Danny's fully-grown hands: Munchie perched on Danny's right hand and Tuffy on his left. Danny had one thumb extended upright. Both cats were purring at full volume. The man-child lay still with the hint of a smile as his own rich purring 'humm' resonated in tune with the cats. Our kitties had found a friend. Maybe Danny had found two.

Don't Judge a Book by its Cover

Our one-night layover in Houston at BigLig's was topped off with an after-dark fireworks display that equaled anything we had ever seen on the Mall in Washington, D.C. It was clear that living next to the Houston Country Club had its perks. We sat at the outdoor table in BigLig's backyard and watched a fortune in oil money explode in colorful rockets directly over our heads. Tuffy and Munchie had scampered from Danny's side at the first boom and were now snuggled away in the back of a closet.

The night was clear and our stomachs were full as we gazed upward at this unending display of pyrotechnics. Earlier, BigLig had saved us from the painful choice of choosing a Houston dinner spot. This part of our trip was totally unscheduled and we, of course, had no advanced reservations at any of the town's highly-rated grub boxes. At 6:30 p.m., BigLig voice dialed two numbers from his office workstation. Thirty seconds later, our dinner dilemma was solved, and BigLig's secretary was on her way to stay with Danny. We had gotten reservations for a July 4th dinner within 30 minutes, with or without cats. BigLig kept the dining destination a surprise.

The three of us, sans kitties, hopped into BigLig's Escalade -- a gift from his son, Jeff, whose genius at knowing how to buy low and sell high had made him a legend in the Houston oil and gas world. We drove away from Westheimer and the Inner Loop and crossed north of the Katy freeway. Alice and I knew the Inner Loop and Westheimer Road was home to the most upscale, trendiest, most unusual and most expensive dining spots in Houston. As America's third largest city, and probably the city richest in personal wealth, the choices in dining were unequaled anywhere outside of Atlanta and New York. Before buying our home in Mexico, we had toyed with the idea of moving to Houston. We had spent six very long holiday weekends at various hotels around the Inner Loop testing out the dining, which invariably involved driving on or crossing over Westheimer Drive.

Alice and I wondered where we were headed as we passed Eddie V's tucked away inside the Gables West micro mall on the corner of Kirby Drive. Eddie V's was a place that served Dungeness crab cocktails in crystal flutes the size of Bavarian beer mugs. Farther down Westheimer, across from Ruth's Chris, stood the home of America's most famous surf and turf offering. At Truluck's, patrons did not order stone crab claws by the plate; they were offered only by the pound – and no half portions, either. For the ethnic tongue, there was Indian opulence at Kiran's. The most spectacular Indian menu this side of Kashmir was overshadowed only by the majesty of the service and the perfection of each dish, which was epitomized by the Kiran Lobster Malabar. Of course, there were the Zagat's and NY Times-heralded spots like B & B Butchers, Black and White, or our favorite meat shop: the Taste of Texas, known for its salad bar that rivaled every

Whole Foods in the state. Alice and I favored this unique urban eatery for its prime rib. The Taste of Texas was the only restaurant we had visited that offered full or half-portion cuts of prime rib that were always ready to be served at the desired doneness: medium, medium-well or rare. This talent for providing cooked perfection for any cut at any hour of the day or night was a restaurant mystery. But we were not heading for Taste of Texas, either. We continued to drive in the opposite direction from each of these culinary landmarks.

After seven or eight minutes, BigLig pulled off Longpoint Road and turned into a small strip center with a handful of stores. The Escalade headlamps illuminated a block-lettered sign over the double-glass door: Hollister Grill. We had arrived. As we crawled down out of the oversized roadster, BigLig stepped around to the car's back gate and pulled out two bottles of wine from a custom-made travel carton. He gave Alice and me a big grin and said, "You are going to like this place." He was right. Hollister Grill is the creation of one man, Chuck Hollister. Chuck, who loved to cook, hit an oil well, retired from the grime and opened a spot that is downtown Houston's most undiscovered gem.

The proprietor and chef opened the door for us and gave BigLig a welcoming hug as he deftly extracted the two bottles of wine from BigLig's hands. There, against the back wall, was an open booth spread with a white tablecloth and set with Herend china, Waterford crystal and a small placard that read 'Reserved Forever.' We pushed into the booth with BigLig squirming his now not-so-big frame into the bench opposite Alice and me.

A BYOB restaurant in a low-rent shopping center fifteen minutes outside the Inner Loop with Waterford crystal and Herend china place servings definitely exceeded our expectations, and we hadn't even seen the menu. I had, however, already seen some of the night's offerings. There was room for about 50 diners with four-person booths along three walls and tables for four and six spaced in the center

69

that accommodated the rest. Every seat was full, and many patrons were enjoying entrees as we made our way to our booth. I spotted chicken and waffles, biscuits lathered in red-eye gravy, shrimp and grits, thick-cut rib-eyes, and lightly battered filets of fish ensconced with multi-colored chard. My nose had picked up a favorite scent, and I was eager to unveil the menu. There it was, at the top of the starters: char-roasted Brussels sprouts. Alice sensed it as well, and we smiled, knowing full well we were going to like Hollister.

As we waited for the sprouts and sipped the Colby red, BigLig shared the story of Hollister. Chuck Hollister loved upscale dining and loved to cook. After he made his fortune, he decided to indulge both his passions, choosing the Longpoint location for two reasons. First was the need for parking. Houston runs on cars. At Hollister Grill, there is enough room to park 50 cars after 5:00 p.m. when the Mom-and-Pop stores in the strip mall close. Second was Chuck's desire to have only dinner guests who really wanted to be there. His Grill was only minutes from the most upscale neighborhood on Memorial Drive.

His solution was a success. On July 4th, every table and chair was filled. It was the same every night of the week, and reservations were only available by phone, upon request, between 1:00 p.m. and 5:00 p.m. each day. Walk-ins were always welcomed, and the small bar offered free iced tea while patrons waited. It dawned on me that Chuck's place was Houston's version of New Orleans' Clancy's. The best way to discover it was to visit with someone who was already familiar with the location and the experience.

Char-Grilled Sprouts

Our sprouts arrived, and I could see my recipe staring me in the face. My own preparation of this dish had come with trial and error. Brussels sprouts are dense, cruciferous veggies in the cabbage family. The dish originated in

Belgium, thus the name. Due to their dense nature, a successful preparation should include two knife cuts. The first cut is to remove the hard little knob at the bottom of each sprout. The second is to cut each sprout down the middle, top to bottom, leaving only the smallest circumference sprouts in their whole state. Next the sprouts should be pre-cooked in a microwave for at least five to seven minutes. This step is not obvious, and if not discovered, the diner quickly learns that frying, alone, even unto charring, will not yield the necessary firm but done texture. Most servings of this dish, when not pre-cooked, leave the diner saying 'it has a great flavor but they seem underdone.' Microwaving beforehand eliminates this complaint. At Hollister, it was certain that Chuck had already discovered this technique.

Next, the sautéing should be done in an open saucepan with a wide, flat bottom. At least two pieces of bacon should be well cooked until crisp, leaving the drippings in the pan. A small white onion, sliced thinly and two cloves of garlic also thinly sliced, should be readied. The cayenne flakes should be on hand, along with hoisin sauce. With everything ready, including the pre-cooked sprouts, it is time to heat four tablespoons of canola oil to high heat until a water drop explodes on contact with the oil. Slide the garlic slices and white onion into the pan, and as soon as the garlic turns translucent, turn down the heat to medium. Remove the pan from the heat as the garlic and onion continue to simmer. After two minutes, the pan should be reset on the heat until the oil touches off spark-like sounds from the garlic and onion once more. Pour in the sprouts immediately, and turn the heat back up to high. Use a spatula or fork to turn as many sprouts as possible onto the flat end that was previously cut and continue cooking on high, watching for the flat sides to turn a dark, smoky brown. Begin stirring the sprouts over high heat, and without allowing the oil or the sprouts to burn, watch as the sprouts begin to darken, and slowly break off into tiny, charred pieces. Sprinkle half a thimble of cayenne flakes into the pan, and crumble and stir in the crisp bacon. Continue stirring until the sprouts start to blacken, and remove from the heat. While they are still in the pan, pour in two ounces of hoisin sauce and stir until the sprouts are lightly coated. Serve immediately.

Dinner, Continued

The three of us were still spooning charred sprouts onto our plates when our server delivered the main dishes. This was my first experience with *Country-Fried Steak*. Chicken-fried steaks were all the rage in diners from Santa Clara to Baltimore, but this was a *Country-Fried Steak*. It lay smoldering on the Herend Rothschild plate under a pile of thinly battered onion rings. Chuck's famous, sixteen-ounce prime rib eye sprawled on the china, powdered in a mica-thin crust of xxx panko bread crumbs and deep fried to a golden brown. My jaws were stinging with anticipation.

Across from me, our server slid a Mediterranean Eat Healthy choice over to BigLig. A red snapper, exquisitely fileted into dual slices and seared ever so slightly on a super-hot iron pan, was spread over rosy lumps of sautéed back-fin crab and shouldered with sweet peas and scallions accompanied by two corn-risotto croquettes.

Alice's order passed in front of me. The saucer bowl-shaped dish was steaming with roasted corn and creamy poblano risotto punctuated with pan-seared scallops and oversized Gulf shrimp. As we each began to tuck into these delights, Chuck stopped by, and without a hint of a smile, leaned in and asked in mess-sergeant style, "Are you gettin' enough to eat?"

Chapter 4 Beaumont, Babe, and Boudin

"Those who'll play with cats must expect to be scratched." Miguel de Cervantes

Sunday morning came early after the Hollister Grill dinner and 4th of July fireworks extravaganza. The Fit was loaded with the rested and well-fed kitties that were in their carriers when BigLig showed up at the kitchen door with toasted bagels and cream cheese. As we walked to the car, he handed me a slip of paper carefully folded in half. It was his suggestion for another dining experience to add to our scheduled list.

During dinner at the Hollister Grill, we had filled BigLig in on most of our travel plans. We agreed to provide him feedback on all the restaurants, as well as report back on the historical sites we had mapped out. Our itinerary listed a short stopover in Beaumont, Texas, to see Spindletop and the Babe Didrikson Zaharias Museum, followed by a half-day's drive around the Gulf corner into Louisiana, with a possible stop overnight in Baton Rouge. BigLig calculated that with an hour layover in Beaumont, we would be passing Lafayette, Louisiana, by 1:00 p.m. He had the perfect spot for lunch. The location wasn't actually in Lafayette but in Scott which, according to BigLig, was the recognized Boudin Capital of the World, and Billy's Boudin and Cracklin was the undisputed champion of boudin kitchens in Scott. With a quick "thank you" for the hospitality and lunch suggestion, we broke off and headed up I-10 toward Beaumont.

Gusher that Changed the World

Ask any eighth grader in Texas to name the two most important events in Texas history, and the answers will be the Alamo and the Cowboys' Super Bowl VI win with Roger Staubach. Before Roger's 1971 victory, the second answer would have been Spindletop. Located three miles from Beaumont's city center, Spindletop was home to the first 100,000-barrel-a-day oil gusher on the planet. We had come to see the site that changed history. Spindletop did more than change Texas; it changed the world. Before Spindletop hit in 1901, the search for oil in Texas was restricted to hordes of wildcatters on borrowed money making hit-or-miss drilling attempts with the most primitive of equipment.

I knew this from my experience as a frequent flier during the booming days of the computer revolution. Much of my knowledge about the Texas petroleum history was gleaned from Delta, Eastern, and Braniff in-flight magazines. Airlines competed for the best articles to keep customers entertained in route. When flying west, articles about Texas oil and Texas money were among the most popular subjects. More than once, I had entertained a bartender and fellow layover friends with my extensive knowledge of Texas oil history-all of which was gained from flight magazines.

By the turn of the century, oil was in high demand. The world ran on oil long before Henry Ford's first Model-T came off the assembly line in 1908. By the end of the Civil War in 1865, the black slippery stuff was the number one lubricant in the world. Every wheel that turned needed oil. Thousands of passenger ships and freighters burned millions of gallons every day while ferrying people and goods across the Atlantic and Pacific oceans. My audience always seemed surprised to learn that before the first supersized gusher at Spindletop, oil in Texas was usually found by searching on the earth's surface. Wildcatters sought out locations where natural seepage produced large but shallow pools of the sticky black stuff. Finding these spots was a challenge. Texas had a lot of barren and hard-to-reach geography, and no one had invented drones to fly over it with GoPro cameras.

Outside of Texas, fortunes were being made from oil discoveries. By 1900 Pennsylvania was already the home of the first petro-millionaires. The Rockefeller fortune was compounding every day on Pennsylvania oil, while half of all Texas wildcatters were going bankrupt. By1900, the world required two million barrels of oil a day, and the best Texas could deliver was two thousand barrels a day. Then Spindletop hit. The well produced 100,000 barrels from the first day forward. This one well on top of a salt dome in Texas spouted 50 times the amount of oil the entire state had been producing. Six months later, over one hundred drilling derricks were plunging bits into the Spindletop salt dome. Every one was a gusher. The petroleum age was born in Beaumont, Texas. Cheap energy had been discovered, and the world has been dependent on it since then.

The modern-day site of Spindletop is actually called Spindletop-Gladys City Boomtown Museum. A few of the original buildings remain, and have been reconfigured to represent a small community complete with soda shop, fire station, sundry supply store, and even a barber shop. Standing in the center is a replica of the original wooden derrick that held the Lucas well-drilling equipment. Anthony Lucas was the pioneering engineer who owned and built the first 100-foot wooden derrick that drove the hydraulic drill bit into the first Spindletop gusher.

The Boomtown Museum features a biography on Lucas who had not been a native Texan wildcatter. Born Antonio Lucich, he was an Austrian who immigrated to the U.S. in his twenties. Eyewitnesses to the Lucas gusher all agreed that the event was a phenomenal occurrence. It seems that the Lucas team had been drilling with some new type of hydraulic-powered bits to bore through the layers of sand that had previously prevented punching through the salt dome. When the drill bit pierced through the sand, it hit a natural gas bowl that was under extreme pressure. As the tip knifed in, the pressure exploded upward through the narrow

75

channel. It blew 16,000 pounds of steel-boring bits and drill shafts up through the hole and wrecked the wooden derrick above. Luckily, the noise preceding this had warned the drillers off the platform so no one was hurt. Moments later, eyewitnesses reported an earthbound rumbling that made them cover their ears. A geyser of oil that shot over 200 feet into the air and required nine days to contain quickly followed. On certain days, The Boomtown Museum treats visitors to a reenactment of the Lucas 1901 gusher. As the reenactment is done with high-pressure water, the demonstration probably doesn't have the same effect as it did on the original spectators.

Next Stop: Mildred Ella

During our short time at Spindletop, the skies had clouded over and we decided it was time to leave. We had left the kitties in the Fit while we traipsed around. They were in the car with the air conditioning on, sun blockers over the heavily tinted windows, and the doors locked. When we got to the car, I could see Munchie standing upright with her paws on the steering wheel while Tuffy sprawled like a melted meatloaf on the wide, Fit dashboard.

Entering the Fit while the kitties were inside was always tricky. Both were certain to spring toward the door the instant the lock popped open. Alice had taught me a patented move to get around this problem. She would stand in clear sight on the passenger's side while I would furtively glide around the rear of the car; bent over and out of sight. Remaining out of kitty sight I would slip next to the driver's side door. Standing at the passenger door, Alice would proceed to snap the lock up and down until both kitties' attention was focused on her. Most likely, they were saying, "Please let me out" in felinese and were set to jump for freedom. That moment was my cue to jerk open the driver's side door and swiftly glide under the wheel while pulling the door shut in one graceful move. The method worked, and the kitties had not yet wised up to the trick. Once inside, both critters would immediately turn their attention to me and rush to my lap to plead for relief. Alice would slyly open the passenger's side door and enter, and the entry maneuver was complete.

With the kitties happily in tow, and raindrops splashing on the windshield, I set the GPS for our next historical Beaumont site. The Hondalink GPS displayed a distance of six miles, and the route took us back the way we came. Within five minutes, the rain, which had started as a pitter-patter, had turned into a Texas frog-strangler of some proportion. Flash flood warnings were ringing over iPhone alerts. High-pitched squeals warning of imminent danger speared the kitties' sensitive ears, and they leapt from our respective laps to the duffle bags in back, leaving deep claw marks in our thighs and seriously unraveling Alice's' new shawl. As I worked to keep the Fit from hydroplaning on the slick roadway, Alice loosened her seat belt and struggled to turn around to comfort Munchie and Tuffy. Both kitties were furiously digging away at the blankets covering the luggage, seeking to escape the shrieking alerts. With little hesitation, I removed the iPhone from its steely ball hanger and pressed the mute button; the noise abruptly ceased. Unfortunately, the GPS also ceased, and I was forced to scan the water-shrouded road for a safe haven while we waited for the rain to pass.

A nearby driveway beckoned. I hit the turn signal and pulled up an inclined concrete drive that ended under a shingle-roofed carport large enough for two vehicles. The gunshot-staccato noise of raindrops on the Fit's sunroof instantly ceased, and the only sound in the Fit was the British lady on the Hondalink GPS repeating, "Make a U turn! Make a U turn!"

With torrents of rain spilling around us, we sat in the car with the engine running, the kitties back in our laps, and the windows fogged up. For a few minutes, we were snuggled up safe and secure in our little Honda cave. Moments later, we heard a quick rapping at my window. I hastily scrubbed the condensate with my bare hand and saw, peering in at us, a face so lined with age it would have challenged Picasso. I lowered the glass a couple of inches and gave a quick, 'Hello' along with my usual warning about cats on the loose. The woman's eyes lit up at the word 'cats,' and she put her face on the glass. Without hesitating, Alice leaned across me to speak to our mysterious stranger. She said we were cat travelers from Mexico caught in a storm. Instantly we were transformed from interlopers to unexpected guests. Our new acquaintance continued to beckon us to follow her as we gathered the kitties in their carriers, exited the car, and followed the woman who introduced herself as Betty James into her home. The rain continued to fall in sheets.

We had arrived on Sunday at 11:30 a.m. at the 1950s bungalow of a distinguished Beaumont citizen. Betty had hot tea and cookies laid out as though she had been expecting us. We accepted this surprising welcome, and waited for her to query us about our unexpected arrival. As it turns out, locals, as well as folks she had never met, arrived at her home unexpectedly on a regular basis. Evidence of those many visitors stuck out conspicuously from every corner of the bay-windowed living room. Signed Hallmark special occasion cards were tacked and taped across the fireplace mantle, giving the room the look of a cheery Christmas morning. The room was overflowing with potted violets and freshly cut yellow day lilies. We wondered aloud who had brought them.

Betty said that they came from friends, strangers, family and some people she didn't remember. Alice and I had no idea what to make of it. Betty must have a worldwide fan club. She informed us that she sometimes received advance notice by mail or a phone call from some stranger who was planning a visit, but usually there was no notice whatsoever. She was accustomed to welcoming new arrivals most any day or night, but especially during the summer months when school was out. These strangers from afar usually brought a gift, sometimes cut flowers or maybe a decorative plant. Betty was always ready with hot tea and cookies.

After passing us the cookies, Betty looked at us and said how happy she was that we had thought to bring our kitties for her to see. She told us that she adored cats, and that Babe had always said, "You can never have too many cats."

I flinched at the mention of the name, 'Babe.' In my research on Babe Didrikson, who had won two Olympic Gold Medals in track, and then won ten major LPGA tournaments, I had come across a 1950s reference to a female golfer named Betty James who was purported to have been Babe's live-in lover. I hadn't thought much of it at the time, but suddenly the news article was back on my radar screen. Could this petite, gray-haired woman wearing silver-framed spectacles be the lady golfer named in the article? She was old enough. Had Alice and I been washed off our track to the Babe Didrikson Museum only to land in the home of Babe's most intimate friend, Betty James?

My face shivered, and a cold chill ran up my spine. We were sitting in Beaumont, Texas, drinking tea, eating cookies, and talking about cats with the one person still living who could tell us more about Babe Didrikson Zaharias than we could ever learn in any museum. Visitors to the museum honoring the World's Greatest Woman Athlete soon learned that Babe's first LPGA partner was an octogenarian who was alive and living in Beaumont. This accounted for all the unexpected but welcome visitors. Now Alice and I sat here, as had so many other unexpected guests, face-to-face with living history. Betty could tell us about the young woman from Beaumont who had become a legend in her own time.

79

By the time Babe Didrikson was 21-years-old, she could run faster, jump higher and throw a javelin farther than any woman – and most men – in the world. She had already been an international teenage basketball sensation and could play every position on a baseball field. The Associated Press had named Babe The Greatest Woman Athlete of All Time before Babe had ever hit a golf ball. Babe, it seems, discovered golf at the age most Olympians retired from athletics. She was soon recognized as the Greatest Woman Golfer in the World.

Betty had met Babe in 1950 at a golf tournament where they were both competing on the new LPGA circuit. Babe was the founder of the Ladies Professional Golf Association that now included Betty James as a founding member. Betty said she could not believe her luck when she found out she had been paired to play at an amateur event in Miami with Babe Didrikson. Babe had already won the last of the three women's Majors of the day, and sports writers were trying to interview her at the moment she was introduced to her young partner, Betty James. Reporters from local newspapers and the AP surrounded the duo when they first shook hands. Betty still remembered blurting out how much she admired Babe and thought she was fabulous and would do anything for her. Betty was almost twenty years younger than Babe, but the two athletes were instantly attracted to each other. Babe did not even wait for the end of the day's match before inviting Betty to come to Tampa to live with her and husband, George Zaharias. Betty continued to live with Babe and George for the next five years until Babe's tragic early death from colon cancer. Babe was only 45 years old. Shortly after her friend's death Betty decided to move to Babe's hometown of Beaumont where in 1956, she initiated the drive for a museum honoring the World's Greatest Female Athlete.

As we were taking this information in Betty interrupted herself to ask about our kitties. I could tell from

80

the decreasing volume of her gravelly voice that she was tiring from the effort to satisfy our obvious curiosity about her relationship with Babe, but she was more interested in our two kitties than in fishing out more old memories. Both Munchie and Tuffy were clawing and whining to leave their carriers when Alice offered to give Betty a closer look. Alice carefully unzipped Tuffy from her Sleepypod.

Solid black with dark eyes to match, Tuffy was the darling of the lap set. She always assumed the best about humans and was content to slouch her sixteen or so pounds slowly around the premises. She studied the three of us carefully, homing in on the most desirable real estate. With one rather graceful hop from the bungalow floor, she nestled into Betty James' lap. As Betty cradled our kitty in both hands, she said that she and Babe had settled for raising cats rather than kids.

This unusual announcement took me by surprise. Alice shot me a 'don't say anything,' glance as Betty continued talking to us about her life with Babe. Babe and George Zaharias had been married for almost twelve years and were living in Tampa when Betty was invited to join them. Babe's husband, George, was quite famous in his own right. He was a 235-pound professional wrestler known on the fledgling professional fight circuit as the "Weeping Greek from Cripple Creek." Cripple Creek was the gold mining camp at the foot of Pike's Peak near George's birthplace in Pueblo, Colorado. George's parents had immigrated from Tripoli, Greece, and George was the first of their children born in the U.S. His constantly pouting expression earned him his nickname as the "Crying Greek" on the wrestling circuit.

George and Babe, not surprisingly, had met playing golf and were married after an eleven-month whirlwind courtship. Unable to start a family on their own, the two professional athletes pursued the adoption route. After several tumultuous years of failing to win approval from adoption agencies, the strain on their marriage took its toll.

It was during this difficult period that the two lady golfers first met. Betty said Babe was distraught over her situation. Babe had proven to the world she was the greatest female golfer by winning seventeen amateur tournaments in a row and winning all three Women's' Majors on the LPGA tour, but she had not been able to prove to adoption authorities she was qualified to be a mother. No longer concerned about the world and her fans' attitudes toward her, the famous athlete gave in to her heart and filled the void with the young and talented Betty James. George, out of incomprehensible love for Babe, had silently moved aside and willingly shared his domicile with Babe's new partner.

As we sat listening, I could not stop thinking how much the world had changed from Babe Didrikson's time to my own. By the time Billy Jean King had come out of the closet, the news barely made it to the third page of the sports section. When Martina Navratilova fessed-up, she couldn't even get a sportswriter to show for the announcement. Today Cheryl Swopes can walk down 5th Avenue hand in hand with her girlfriend and no one even notices. I would not have thought the change in social attitude was that radical until Betty pointed to one of the faded, yellow sports clippings in her scrapbook. It was a quote from a sports writer working for the New York Telegram during the 1930s when Babe was making history in every sport.

The quote read, "It would be much better if she and her ilk stayed home, got themselves prettied up and waited for the phone to ring." This was from the same sports writer who was famous for having claimed he saw Babe Ruth point to the stands before hitting his home run in the 1932 World Series. The word "ilk" got my blood boiling. "Outrageous," I muttered under my breath. Alice shot me another of her 'hush' looks. She knew how perturbed I could become over a shameless remark about a person's sexuality – even one that had been made over half a century ago. I wondered if my parents, who had been sports enthusiasts, had been aware of the Sapphic side of Babe.

My childhood days had always ended around the dinner table. Dinner conversation usually touched on baseball or golf. My parents seldom missed a Brooklyn Dodgers radio broadcast. When it came to golf, they never agreed on anything except when it came to Babe Didrikson. Mom and Dad had been raised an hour away from the storied fairways of the Augusta National Golf Club, and golf was in their blood. Dad and his older brother, Steel Roy, had stood shoulder to shoulder watching Gene Sarazen's double-eagle put the Masters on the map. His phenomenal tie for the lead in the Masters with a second shot on the fifteenth hole was the first "shot heard round the world." This was Sarazen's four-wood smash from the fairway that flew 235 yards and rolled in for a double eagle on the par five Firethorn.

Three weeks after witnessing Sarazen's miraculous shot, my dad's eyes lit up over the headlines in the sports section. The Atlanta Constitution reported that Olympic Champion Babe Didrikson had driven the ball 260 yards from the first tee at Indian Hills and went on to win her match with a seven under par. The great Byron Nelson remarked only a handful of men alive could outdrive Babe Didrikson. The lady golfer and Olympic champion immediately became one of my dad's favorite sports heroes.

Considering how captivated my parents had been by sports celebrities, I shouldn't have been surprised that my childhood dinner conversations involved so many sports analogies. In grade school, I could count on hearing how hitting like Babe Ruth or jumping like Babe Didrikson somehow equated to making better grades in long division and spelling. While there was plenty of talk about home runs and bases stolen, there was none about the lives of the athletes behind those records. I learned more about Babe

83

Didrikson listening to Betty's reminisces than I had ever heard around the dinner table at home.

My parents had been impressed with achievements and records and helping me understand how much preparation and training preceded the storied event. This was their way of teaching me that it was necessary to practice in order to succeed in life. From my mom, I also learned that records were made to be broken by those who had the talent and could afford the price. My dad taught me to respect my own capabilities and know my limits. His wish, I suppose, was to teach me to love the effort, not the goals. Looking back, I think it was his way of telling me that life was about the journey and not the destination. Babe's athletic prowess was held up to me as an example of success through hard work.

Sitting beside Betty, I wondered how many female college students in America were aware of the debt they owed to Babe Didrikson. Babe died sixteen years before Title IX law passed in 1972, ending discrimination on the basis of sex in federally-funded education programs and activities. No longer were athletic scholarships the exclusive reward for physically talented high school boys.

Betty asked if I wanted to see other mementos she had brought from the Tampa home she had shared with Babe and George Zaharias during the last few years of Babe's life. The rain had stopped, and all the firsthand Babe stories had rekindled my interest in getting to the museum. I confessed as much, but Betty told me the museum was closed on Sundays. So much for preparation. Alice could not conceal her laughter, though I couldn't hide my disappointment. Betty slid the fat fur ball off her lap, stood and beckoned me to follow. She thought I might enjoy seeing some of the memorabilia

As we stepped into the back parlor, Betty pointed out a pair of gold shoes, mounted on a metal trophy stand that Babe had worn when she had won the Dead Head Trophy.

'Dead Head' was the name of the Women's' World Golf Championship, and Babe had to win it three times to win the trophy. Next I saw, suspended in a glass case, three Olympic medals – two gold and one silver. They were from Babe's successful 1932 Olympics. I smiled as I read aloud the award letter made out to Mildred Ella Didrikson – Babe's given name. Farther along the wall I saw the trophy and medallion Babe received as founder of the LPGA: The Ladies Professional Golf Association.

Alice was holding Tuffy and poking through some other items when she noticed a disk mounted on the wall. Beautifully matted onto a polished wooden background was a 45-rpm record released in January of 1955. The Mercury Record label was imprinted with the title, "*I Felt a Little Teardrop,*" with vocals by Betty James and accompaniment by Babe Zaharias on harmonica. Here was another side of Babe I'll bet that hardly anyone had ever known about. Betty smiled and said that the instrumentals were much better than the vocals. Somehow, I doubted that, but it was interesting to see that the name "Babe" was powerful enough to sell a harmonica record.

Betty was still pointing out items when I asked what was in the museum if all these items were here in the house. She told me that the museum houses mostly replicas of the originals that we were now seeing. Seems we didn't miss the museum after all.

Our time for visiting was running out. Alice put a tired Tuffy into her carrier, and scooped up a sleeping Munchie. Before we departed, I had one more question for Betty: what did she think about the movie, *Babe*? (I wasn't referring to the movie about a pig raised by sheepdogs but rather the one made in 1975 about the life of Babe Didrikson Zaharias. It starred Susan Clark as Babe and Alex Karras as George Zaharias.) Betty said she had loved it.

As we said our goodbyes, Betty inquired about our lunch plans. Not wishing to be rude, I told her only that we were late in leaving for Baton Rouge and probably would pass on lunch. She said that if we changed our minds, we would probably really enjoy a spot up the road about an hour-and-a-half away. Many of her visitors had mentioned it to her as a popular stopping point on the way to Baton Rouge. She said it was just over the state line in Scott, right on the interstate. The place was called Billy's Boudin and Cracklin.

Chapter 5: Boudin Wars

"The mice which helplessly find themselves between the cats' teeth acquire no merit from their enforced sacrifice." Mahatma Gandhi

By the time we pulled onto Interstate 10, both kitties were out of their carriers and seeking attention. Alice could only placate one at a time. Tuffy was the easiest in the sense that any lap would suffice, but picking up the fat-bottomed girl was like getting your hands around a pillowcase filled with sand. She intentionally stretched out and let each end of her body hang down. In contrast, Munchie was a lightweight. She had the heft of two pairs of socks, but she was quick. Alice said we should rename her Lightning. More than once I have seen her spring from a prone position to the top bench of her cat tree. The reason we kept our car windows shut and carefully entered and exited our vehicle with stealth was in deference to the speed demon that was, at the moment, jumping back and forth between my lap and the dashboard.

Munchie and the iPad

When she wasn't jumping, Munchie would train her attention on my hands on the steering wheel. Each tiny nudge of the wheel activated the little speed demon. After a few flicks of her tail, she would jump toward the steering wheel, grab hold with both paws, and dangle down loosely, urging me to turn the wheel back and forth to rock the Fit from side to side. Perhaps Munchie was imitating the Saturday Night Live skit made famous by Steve Martin and Victoria Jackson when Tunsis the gray-striped tabby proved he could drive the car – just not very well. Recognizing the danger of this behavior, Alice, who was accomplished in the field of kitty psychology, discovered a remedy.

She diagnosed Munchie as suffering from KDD or Kitty Deficit Disorder. It was similar to ADHD that afflicts grade school kids, but KDD required a different kind of treatment. In Munchie's case, the solution was to 'feed' the impulsiveness by activating the *Bird Spotters Bible* on an iPad. Before I could peel Munchie off the wheel, Alice had summoned from the iPad the unmistakable tweet of a Northern Lark. Hearing it, Munchie was off the wheel and flattened her body on the center armrest, keeping her eyes fixed on the flashing iPad screen. The only movement was the uncontrollable twitch at the tip of her gray-streaked tail.

As each new bird species appeared in full color on the screen and warbled, tweeted, or shrieked its native call, Munchie remained motionless and fixed on the image. As long as she didn't try to jump the bird on the screen, we could drive on in peace. So far, she had been satisfied with posing for the hunt without ever going in for the kill.

Our soggy morning slowly morphed into a clear blue sky with the hot Texas sun steaming the water off the road. With barely 60 miles to go to Scott, we got the first hint of our destination. A billboard the size of the Redskins' JumboTron was flashing the number '97' in huge digits. The numbers pulsed on and off without a hint as to the meaning.

We passed two more billboards displaying the same two digits before finally being treated to a clue: "Exit 97." No distance or destination was listed, only "Exit 97." Alice did not wait for me to ask her to check into this, but already had her iPhone activated with the Hondalink map up on the screen. Exit 97 was for Scott, Louisiana, 30 miles north.

A blizzard of billboards began popping up along Interstate 10. Each urged us to take Exit 97 and eat at a named local dining spot. The flashing digits had been demystified; it was the path to 'Boudin Nirvana' where every street corner featured someone's favorite dining spot. Cars and trucks slowed to a crawl while attempting to read all the propaganda. Finally, a colorful billboard decked out in red,

88

white, and blue that stood out from all the others proudly proclaimed: "Welcome to Scott, Boudin Capital of the World." This was a claim we were in no position to dispute, but we soon discovered that others did.

A plethora of purveyors challenged us to test their claims of offering the most succulent sausage. Luckily, we had a recommendation from BigLig that was confirmed by Betty James. Otherwise, it might have been difficult to choose among Clyde's World Famous, Earline's Finest, Purvis Pure Eatin', Mack's Smakin' Good, Miss Joy's Heavenly, or one of the other 20 boudin purveyors in Scott.

Pulling into the right lane, my head swiveled as it caught sight of the final ad for Exit 97. Stretched across the exit lane was a thirty-foot wide smile painted on a yellow background that heralded Billy's Boudin and Cracklin as the winner, for the fifth year in a row, of the Scott, Louisiana, 'Boudin Festival and Taste Off.' Apparently, the festival winner was entitled to the choicest signage spot on the exit.

The Road to Billy's Boudin

Had we known what awaited us at the end of Exit 97, we would have stayed in the left lane and continued on (lunch less) to Baton Rouge. But once we had committed ourselves to the right lane, there was no way to return to Interstate 10 without running the boudin gauntlet. The exit ramp took us up a slight incline to Apollo Road, which crossed over I-10 and led directly into the town of Scott, but the line of cars moving slowly through the stop sign and turning right onto Apollo Road hindered our progress.

The line of cars along Apollo Road was astonishingly polite considering the crowd. Each car yielded 'uno a uno' so that cars from the exit ramp could filter into the lane. From the stop sign, the road into Scott ran down a slight hill that afforded us a clear view of what lay ahead. A line of cars snaked down the hill for over half a mile to a roundabout in the center of Apollo Road with offshoots into town from the opposite end. Along both sides of the road were cinderblock buildings of various shapes. Most were one-story tall, but at the bottom of the hill, Billy's Boudin and Cracklin rose two stories high with a rollout cloth awning that extended almost to the road. A few cars in front of us turned out of line, but most seemed headed to one destination – Billy's Boudin.

But now the line stopped moving. Billy's lot was full. No one could enter until Billy's current boudin eaters departed. This was bad, but it got worse. Along each side of the road were small, sunshade tarpaulins. These were way-stations on route to the boudin shacks. Every tarp had promoters tasked with getting the now-stranded motorists to choose their boudin joint. Alice and I were amazed until we realized how aggressively these boudin promoters trolled for customers. What we had at first thought were car passengers strolling along the roadside amidst an intense traffic jam were, in fact, roving bands of boudin promoters, intent on winning our business. "At this rate, we'll never make it to Baton Rouge for dinner," Alice lamented. Her concern caught my attention. Baton Rouge was less than two hours away so a slight detour at Billy's was nothing to be concerned over. But Alice was concerned. She kept staring out the window and I could tell something else was on her mind. She pointed to the median alongside where groups of aggressive boudin salesmen walked beside the line of cars.

"Those men in T-shirts are trying to intimidate the drivers," she said.

I followed her glance. Alice was right. I could see the smiles on the promoters' faces but they were menacing smiles intended to provoke the stranded drivers. I thought it best to forego our Billy's excursion and break away. There was only one problem. We were stuck in the line of cars along with everyone else.

We would need some outside help in order to break away from the jam. I spotted two promoters in bright green

90

T-shirts emblazoned with "Broussard, Louisiana—Former Boudin Capital of the World" screen-printed across the front. On the backs of the shirts was printed: "Absolutely best boudin in the world, and pretty good crackling, too. The ambiance is decidedly gas-station, but the boudin...."

Struck by the sheer verve of these promoters who had the courage to hawk a competing town's boudin right in the heart of Scott, I made a fateful decision. I turned on the hazard blinkers, lowered the window slightly, extended my arm, and signaled to the two Broussard vendors. Alice looked at me with a perplexed look that meant 'I'm not going to ask, but you had better tell me what you're thinking.' I could only plead for her to trust me as the Broussard men hustled up the road to our car. They carried bulky cloth bags slung over their shoulders and a sheaf of advertising flyers rolled up in one hand. The older of the two men leaned toward my window.

I asked how to get to Broussard, and he began chuckling.

"Why did we want to go to Broussard?" he asked.

I said, "To taste the absolutely best boudin in the world."

"Don't have to go there," he said, and pulled from the cloth bag a large brown sack printed with "Billeaud's Grocery and Market." He held it up to the window. The smell of sausage and pigskins wafted through the Fit. Fresh grease stains seeped from the bulging sack.

"How much?" I asked.

"How much you wanna' pay?"

I offered him $20 for the sack if he and his buddy would stop traffic in the other lane so I could get to the exit ramp.

Without a word, his buddy stepped in front of traffic and carved out a spot for me. Alice stuck a $20 bill in my hand, and I handed it to the man from Broussard, who jammed the sack through the car's window.

"Don't forget to Yelp us," he said, as I steered the Fit down the ramp toward Baton Rouge. We were back on the interstate. Alice patted my hand on the wheel.

"Hubby," she said, "that was one of the three smartest things you've ever done." I glanced over with my quirky smile that said I would not ask and she need not tell, even though I wondered what the two other smart things might have been.

Boudin Wars

Our drive the rest of the way to Baton Rouge lasted about as long as our lunch of Billeauds' Louisiana boudin and cracklins. Alice unrolled one of the promotional flyers to reveal a *Southern Living* write-up on the boudin battle raging between Broussard and Scott. Each of the Cajun communities claimed to be the birthplace of Louisiana boudin. Broussard had, in fact, held the undisputed title for almost 100 years as the north corner of Main Street in Broussard had been the site of Billeaud's family grocery and meat market. After several unsuccessful attempts to unseat the Billeaud claim as the birthplace of boudin, the Scott sausage stuffers decided to go after the claim in earnest. *Southern Living* pointed out that the rivalry had been in good fun up until Scott raised the stakes, and suddenly the friendly rivalry turned deadly serious. The bad blood had begun to boil a couple of years ago during the Lafayette annual 'Boudin Cook-off Festival.'

Both towns, Broussard and Scott, had profited from their friendly rivalry in challenging for the recognition of "Best Boudin." Broussard fed the hungry hordes in the fall, and Scott brought in thousands to taste their pork and rice concoctions during the spring. The friendly competition took a sudden turn for the worse at the end of 'Scott's Springtime Boudin Festival' in 2012. The last day always concluded with the announcement of the winner and the presentation of the award for 'Best Boudin.' Billy's Boudin and Cracklin was the only venue large enough to hold the crowd that squeezed inside the cavernous buffet hall for the announcement.

Among the crowd were boudin eaters and boudin purveyors from all across the Lafayette Parish. Particularly noteworthy was the presence of the Delhomme and Bourque families. The Delhommes were original settlers in Scott but had relocated in a huff to Broussard after the community incorporated and chose to name itself after J.B. Scott, the division superintendent of the Union and Pacific Railroad. The Bourque family lived and some would say 'presided over,' the adjoining township of Jennings, Louisiana. The Bourques pretty much owned the crayfish business west of Baton Rouge, and the Jennings Mayor's office had been occupied by one or another Bourque since 1903. Both families had benefited directly and indirectly from the boudin rivalry that had grown to identify Lafayette Parish and its vibrant Cajun townships: Jennings, Broussard, and Scott.

Friends, family, and far-flung relatives had witnessed the economic miracle of Lafayette Parish that had been born on pork shoulders, livers and the Cajun spices of Louisiana boudin. Protecting and nurturing their livelihoods was paramount in each community. Feigning sausage rivalries among the different towns had paid off for everyone until the announcement in 2012 of the 'Best Boudin.'

It was a foregone conclusion that Billy's Boudin and Cracklin would retain the gold-embossed blue ribbon for 'Best Boudin.' This honor was by agreement awarded to a different Boudin venue every two years. This would be Billy's second year so the announcement of Billy's retention of the award was no surprise. What did surprise everyone, however, was who the announcer of the award was and what he had to say about the town of Scott. Previously, the honor of announcing the winner went to the sitting Mayor of Lafayette. But in 2012, the Speaker of the House from the state legislature of Louisiana was on hand to announce the honor. Mr. Speaker rose from his narrow bench seat on the bandstand riser. What he said was shocking. "By official act of the State Legislature of the State of Louisiana, the town of Scott, Louisiana, will henceforth be known as the 'Official Boudin Capital of the World.'"

The Speaker's words ignited anarchy. Chairs were overturned, and cans of Pabst Blue Ribbon were hurled toward the podium as Delhomme men, and a few Bourque women, charged the podium, hollering "payoff" and "bribery." While jumping from the risers and attempting to escape the incensed crowd, the Speaker tripped and broke his wrist. Choosing one community out of all the contenders and stamping it with the State Seal of "Official Boudin Capital of the World" was more than an insult – it was financial treachery. The upstate visitors in their summer poplin suits were hounded to their waiting vans and private cars.

Now, two years after the Speaker's announcement, the worst was over, and even the Delhomme family accepted Scott as the "Official Boudin Capital of the World." New, welcoming signs had been installed at the gates of Broussard and Jennings, which Billy's Boudin and Cracklin had graciously agreed to pay for. Visitors were now treated to Broussard's "Welcome to the Former Boudin Capital of the World," while Jennings residents claimed, "Welcome to the Boudin Capital of the Universe."

Alice and I concurred with the *Southern Living* article that the dispute was not going to be settled by dueling signs. Alice agreed with me that Broussard deserved at least an honorable mention. We had enjoyed Billeaud's boudin balls and boudin sausage in the traditional style: smoked with the delicate flavor of the pork not overshadowed by the Cajun spices. The boudin sausage was tightly packed in casings that had been fired over an open flame to give the wrapper a fresh, crisp feel. The pork was finely ground, and the texture was smooth to the tongue. The rice and sausage mix squeezed out in perfect chunks. Alice and I offered up a few morsels to Tuffy who, rather than turning up her nose, gobbled down every bite. Munchie, the picky lobster eater, sniffed and nuzzled the lump of dark-smelling protein until she had carefully teased out every grain of Cajun rice, which she lapped up with her pink tongue. According to the kitties, Billeaud's won by a whisker.

Alice carefully tore off and folded the recipe printed on the back panel of Billeaud's flyer. I suggested it might be easier to visit one of Donald Link's New Orleans spots, such as Cochon or Herbsaint and taste his boudin rather than cooking up three pounds of pork products according to his recipe. She smiled and said it was for Tuffy.

Donald Link shared this recipe as part of a special Mardi Gras celebration he created for Epicureans.

Boudin Recipe

2 lb. boneless pork shoulder, cut into 1-inch cubes
1/2 lb. pork liver, cut into 1-inch cubes
1 small onion, chopped
2 celery stalks, chopped
1 med. poblano chili, stemmed, seeded, and chopped
3 med. jalapeño peppers, stemmed, seeded, and chopped
6 garlic cloves, coarsely chopped
4 tbsp. kosher salt
1 tbsp. ground black pepper
1 tbsp. ground white pepper
1 tsp. curing salt
1 tsp. cayenne pepper
1 tsp. chili powder
7 cups cooked white rice
1 cup chopped fresh parsley
1 cup chopped scallions (green and white parts)
4 to 6 feet of sausage casings (optional), rinsed

Combine the pork, liver, vegetables, and seasonings in a bowl and marinate covered, in the refrigerator, for one hour or overnight. Place the marinated mixture in a large pot, and cover the meat with one-two inches of water. Bring the mixture to a boil, reduce the heat, and simmer until the meat is tender – about one hour and 45 minutes. Remove the pot from the heat and strain, reserving the liquid. Allow the mixture to cool slightly, then put the solids through a meat grinder set on a coarse grind. (If you don't have a meat grinder, you can always chop the meat with a knife, which is what I usually do, anyway.) Place the ground meat in a large bowl. Using a wooden spoon or rubber spatula, mix in the cooked rice, parsley, scallions, and reserved cooking liquid. Stir vigorously for five minutes. When the boudin-rice mixture is first combined, it looks very wet, and it's pretty spicy. Don't worry; after poaching, the rice will absorb the excess moisture and much of the spice. The wet texture and extra spice ensure that your final boudin will be moist and full of flavor. At this point, you can feed the sausage into the casings. Poach the links gently in hot (not bubbling) water for about ten minutes, then serve. Alternatively, you can use the mixture as a stuffing for chicken, or roll it into "boudin balls," dredge in bread crumbs, and fry in hot oil until golden brown.

Chapter 6: Our First Kiss

"In nine lifetimes, you'll never know as much about your cat as your cat knows about you." Michel de Montaigne

We joined an ever-lengthening caravan of cars, trucks and buses headed east toward the Mississippi. Munchie and Tuffy were squirming in and out around the luggage. After locating the perfect spot, each kitty took up a preening pose. They politely washed their respective faces and licked their paws in celebration of their boudin snacks.

I looked over at Alice to see if she had any idea what our two felines might be thinking. They were traveling down the highway at almost 70 miles per hour. Semi-trucks hauling steel bars, concrete trusses and silver tanks of flammable liquids streamed by us even faster. Mom and Dad sat up front jawboning about trips they had taken and unusual people they had met. What did our cats think about all this?

Alice looked at me with her little smile and said, "Our cats don't think. Our cats convince." She explained that from the moment a cat makes contact with a human, the feline brain shifts into 'convince' mode. Hearing this for the first time, I gave out an intelligent sounding 'hmm' to let Alice know I was a little unclear on this 'convince' mode thing.

She continued. "The cat is always trying to convince a human of something. At first glance, a cat will appear to be highly independent, intent on owning its space and making its own way in the world. They project an air of indifference, almost aloofness. It is all fakery; 'kitty camouflage'. By nature, cats are anything but independent. By design they must sleep eighteen hours a day. Cats have convinced us to act as their protectors while they sleep."

A Cat's Primary Mission

Alice entreated me to look at our cats as examples. A quick glance in the rear-view mirror showed our cats to be splayed out, sleeping atop our Jansport backpacks. They didn't appear to be exerting effort in the 'convince' mode. I made this point.

"Of course not," Alice responded. "Munchie and Tuffy have already finished convincing us. They are done, *tout a fait.* From the moment they met us, they began to convince us that they were the masters and we were the servants. They spent their waking hours training us to take care of them. Munchie convinced us that the bedroom door must always be open, while Tuffy convinced us that her bowl must always be filled with IAMS. They both convinced us of their importance and worthiness to be served."

I thought of the pharaohs of Egypt. Those ancient sovereigns were majestic rulers of all nations, builders of pyramids, masters of all, and yet still servants of cats. They worshipped them. If there was any thinking going on in those kitty minds, it must have to do with keeping humans on board with this remarkable relationship.

I remembered Tuffy's subtle paw work in bringing me around. Her method was direct and simple. She hops aboard the tallest chair or bureau to bring herself even with my face and stares directly into my eyes with her own green and black orbs. She keeps me locked in this gaze as tiny yelps signal to me to pay attention, which I do. Then she guides me along the hallway to her bowl and leads me to a soft chair, convincing me that it is time for a lap to be presented to her. Alice couldn't stop chortling as I relayed all this to her. She thought it was about time that I finally acknowledged who really had the upper hand in this cat-and-human relationship.

Our Hondalink GPS labeled the highway ahead of us with a solid red line, which meant traffic. Alice and I didn't need the GPS to tell us what we could see. We were jammed into a double lane of cars that were slowing to a crawl as we inched our way to the Mississippi crossing. Both kitties were now standing, paws up against a window and staring intently at the four-door, F-150 pickup truck traveling next to us. Three kids in the back seat of the Ford had spotted Munchie and Tuffy and were waving and pointing as if they had never seen cats travel by car.

Alice wanted to know how long it might take us to reach the Mississippi. I calculated that at the present rate of five miles per hour, it would take about an hour. Except for the frustration of sitting in traffic, the delay was not critical. After leaving Scott, we had made the decision to spend the night in Baton Rouge rather than continuing on to New Orleans. Tonight would be one of Alice's 'backup stops.' She had planned our trip to include unscheduled delays; making it to New Orleans in one day had always been a 'possible' rather than a 'must-do.'

Besides, we had debated the merits of including Baton Rouge as one of our original travel and dining cities. Baton Rouge was where Alice and I had first kissed. As we sat at home in Mexico planning our route, we had decided not to let sentimentality determine our trip. But as we drew nearer to the 'Red Stick,' we couldn't deny a certain excitement in returning to the spot that had kindled our relationship. Memories tend to dim after 35 years, but I could tell from Alice's expression that she remembered our time in Baton Rouge together as well as I did.

Finding Alice

Baton Rouge was not the first time or place I had met Alice, but it was the first place I had kissed her. We had first met in the glass-and-steel offices of the accounting and consulting firm where Alice was the new Director. At the time, it had been one of the 'Big Eight' accounting firms and was considered to be the most prestigious accounting partnership with the largest roster of Fortune 500, blue-chip clients and large government agencies. Alice was a newly minted Ivy League MBA with a BS in computer science. The firm had wined and dined her, and ultimately won in its effort to recruit Alice into its notoriously chauvinistic management consulting practice. She had been in the New York office for most of the year before transferring to Washington D.C.

I was a computer project leader for a fast-growing high-technology firm that was famous for installing the first large-scale IBM financial-accounting systems for New York city and Washington, D.C. Both cities had been on the verge of bankruptcy, and my company had built the computer systems that saved them. Those systems were so complex and difficult to implement that the accounting and consulting firm that Alice worked for was hired to manage and oversee the process. Alice had been selected to be her firm's manager on the next big project that my company was about to undertake. I would be the computer project leader. Together, Alice and I would be in charge of installing a large-scale IBM financial-accounting system in Baton Rouge for the State of Louisiana.

My thoughts slipped back over thirty years to a stormy July afternoon as I exited a yellow cab on the corner of 18th and M Streets in downtown D.C. I brushed the rain from my soaking-wet suit jacket and pulled a crumpled message from my pocket. Alice had left a voicemail at my office naming a time and place for our first meeting. She was new to the D.C. office, and none of my acquaintances knew anything about her. I anticipated the usual stuffed-shirt accounting type masquerading as a management consultant and expected that our meeting would be the usual quick exchange of name, rank and serial number. The working arrangement involved Alice's firm minding its own knitting while we minded ours. If anything went wrong, it was

100

understood that I would blame Alice and Alice would blame me.

When the elevator door opened on the ninth floor, I had my suit jacket off, my red-striped tie dangling under my chin and was shaking the water out of both shoes. I hopped in my stocking feet out of the elevator and onto the slick, tiled floor where I slid clumsily into the arms of my future bride. Absorbing my circumstances in one quick glance, Alice began to laugh. Her unpretentious laugh enchanted me instantly. Alice led me down the hall to her corner office with a window that overlooked 18th and M Streets. In firms like hers, only partners had such accommodations, not new managers fresh out of business school. Taking note of my surprised look, she quickly corrected my misunderstanding. The office was a loaner until suitable digs could be found for Alice, who had been promoted to fill a new position at the firm's D.C. office. She extended a buff, white business card with her name on it and her position listed as 'Liaison Director for Partner Activities.' As I sat in a brown leather club chair adjusting my tie and reassembling my wardrobe, Alice leaned back against the wide mahogany desk, placed her hands behind her, and crossed one leg over the other at the ankle. She remained motionless, without speaking, as she waited for me to finish assessing everything from her blondish bob to the Joan and David shoes lightly strapped across her ankles.

Alice was dressed seriously for business. Female MBAs at her firm were all about outdoing their male colleagues in everything, from achievement to work ethic to professional dress. These were the young women challenging the hegemony of all the male-dominated companies. Her firm had adapted more quickly than most, and Alice was at the forefront of the change. The glass ceiling was seriously cracked, and Alice was hell bent on breaking it for good. Looking at her, I thought she had a good chance of pulling it off.

Her blue pin-striped jacket and skirt was not cut like a Macy's outfit, but was more custom-looking, like a Barney's suit. As she leaned back, her jacket revealed a slender figure that hinted at a commitment to Jazzercise. She wore a long-sleeved silk blouse that was open at the neck with a batik-print scarf that perfectly accented the suit. Tiny diamond studs sparkled off her ears, and I was sure that if she unbuttoned just the top button of her blouse, I would see a single row of Mikimoto pearls peeking out. I quickly checked; there was no ring on her finger. I rubbed my own empty digit. Sitting in front of her, ringing out my linen jacket, I was completely taken in by her casual manner that radiated self-assurance. I liked this woman.

All of these memories were coursing through me as we began to pick up speed in our Mississippi caravan. Alice asked why I was smiling, and I told her what I had been thinking. Alice remembered that first meeting, as well.

She had had the advantage at the time. She had anticipated my arrival with a bit of G2 intelligence in her pocket. Her closest girlfriend in grad school was a bona fide computer whiz from Carnegie Mellon who had been successfully wined and dined by my own firm.

Alice Has a Spy

By our first meeting, Alice had been thoroughly briefed about me. Her friend told her to expect a tall, dark, handsome and cocky drink of water whose accent was so thick the word 'pie' took three syllables to pronounce. She also told Alice that I was single, straight and had a good job. When I crashed into Alice that first day, she thought that my showing up, dripping wet, in my stocking feet was a great introduction. That was the first of many meetings between us as we created our plans for the Baton Rouge project.

We had agreed to divide our prep meetings between her firm's offices and mine. Sessions always started in the afternoon in case we had to work late. Before the end of July, Alice and I had enjoyed half dozen or so lengthy meetings

After each and every meeting, I asked Alice to join me for dinner or drinks. Whenever we worked late at my office, she declined my invitation. The three times we worked late at her office, she accepted my invitation under the condition that she pick up the tab.

Mr. K's on the corner of 19th and M Street was always the destination. Alice and I both liked Chinese food, and Mr. K's was known for creating some very sophisticated cocktails. Each time we left her office for dinner, one or two of Alice's female colleagues would mysteriously appear at the entrance to Mr. K's. The first time this happened, I thought nothing of it when Alice invited her friends to join us (although I was a little surprised that they agreed). The second time they appeared, I asked Alice if we could skip inviting them. Alice thought it would be rude. The third time we ended up at Mr. K's as a foursome, I began to wonder if Alice was at all interested in my company.

I was enjoying these memories from times past as the Fit coasted slowly in the dense traffic that had bunched up on the west side of the river. Alice jerked me back to the present with a sharp and very loud sneeze. I glanced over as four quick, follow-up blasts shook the car. Throwing out my Germanic response "may the spirits of your ancestors leave your body" seemed to make her attack even worse. Alice's sneezing attacks always sent me into paroxysms of laughter. My urge to laugh was amplified by Munchie's reaction. Before Alice could wipe her nose, our speedy Maine Coon had leapt from the rear cargo hold, claws extended and landed in the center console with her paws on top of the shifter. Munchie stretched as much as she could to push her nose within inches of Alice's.

Something in the sound of sneezing always drove our pretty kitty into a state of feline delirium. Munchie would fly out of her deepest hiding spot and race to Alice in an insane attempt to hiss the sneezes back into her mistress. I christened those moments "exorcism by cat" because Munchie clearly thought that sneezes were signs of demonic possession. Now that she had restored order to the universe, the demur lightweight turned tail toward Alice as if to say, "And don't let it happen again," and leapt into the back of the Fit.

The Other Woman

My thoughts drifted back to when Alice and I had made our first trip to Baton Rouge to kick off the financial systems project. We would each be staying at the Heidelberg Hotel. A week had passed since I had last seen Alice, but I managed to get her on the phone every day to talk business. She had seen right through my feeble attempts to maintain contact with her, but continued to take my calls. During the last call, I asked about taking her to dinner the first night we would be staying at the Heidelberg and received only "We'll see" for an answer. It wasn't a definite no, which I chose to interpret as a good sign.

I was uncertain about Alice's feelings (if any) toward me. I didn't know at that time that Alice's friend was keeping an eye on my comings and goings. Had I known about the spy, I would have been more cautious about meeting a particular female in our building's lobby after work. Alice's friend had seen me leave the office on several occasions with my arm around a brunette who had a firm hold on me and had reported her observations to Alice. Hearing about my possible involvement with another woman, Alice was determined to keep me at arm's length. She later told me that she didn't want to complicate her life or mine.

In fact, there was another woman. She was a former girlfriend whom I had met while working in Chicago. She was as Southern as Carolina barbecue, and knew the words to every Willie Nelson song. I had met her while standing on the corner one Saturday afternoon looking at Chicago's historical water tower and pumping station. We were both snapping pictures of the ornate-looking edifice when we happened to turn our cameras on each other. I was a bit homesick for anything Southern, and this woman fit the bill. A few months later, we were a serious item. We moved into a modern, newly-appointed apartment at Lake Point Tower on Navy Pier before I discovered she was suffering from a debilitating Motor Neuron Disease.

We had been living together only a month when she revealed the truth to me. Motor Neuron Disease, or MND, and its worse version, ALS (Amyotrophic Lateral Sclerosis, or Lou Gehrig's disease), sometimes slowly and sometimes quickly choked the life out of the suffering victim. My army comrade and unit captain had been diagnosed with ALS while waiting to be promoted to major. I had visited him at his home in Apple Valley, Wisconsin, and had seen how the disease rapidly destroyed his nervous system. He had already lost the ability to raise his arms or walk, and his ability to swallow was failing. Sometimes, the disease punishes the sufferer for a decade while at other times the suffering is swift and final. When my girlfriend gave me this news, the picture of my former captain flashed in my memory. She had received the definitive diagnosis six months before we met. She had not told me sooner out of fear that I would break up with her. Then she said there was more she had to tell me. I wondered what more there could be after telling your lover you were dying from an incurable disease that would leave you struggling to breathe while your loved one could only stand by helplessly and watch your ungodly suffering.

"I'm leaving you," she said matter of factly, without a hint of sadness or anger. Apparently, she had thought about it ever since the day we moved in together. "I can't stay with a man who would love me out of pity."

Before my words could form, she leaned in and kissed me, stood up and walked to the door with her coat folded over her arm. She said she would call and let me know where she was after she got settled.

The door closed and she was gone. I looked around. Her closet was empty. Her guitar was missing. Her pictures of her mom and dad and her hairbrushes and combs next to our dresser were all gone. She had spent the day packing and moving her life out of mine while I was at work. She had sensed that I would say it was okay, that I would lie to keep her with me. She wanted to spare me from myself by making the decision for both of us.

The next day, the receptionist at her office told me that she had transferred to the LA branch. I left messages for her for the next few days but she didn't respond. I sent a bouquet of red roses with a note telling her that she had broken my heart and to please come back. She didn't acknowledge the note or the flowers.

Two years after this painful experience, I took a call and instantly recognized her voice. She was in Washington D.C. and living at the government's expense on the National Institutes of Health (NIH) campus in Bethesda, Maryland. She wanted to know if I would meet her at Tivoli's bakery in Rosslyn just to say hello. This was the same week that I had met Alice in the rain. During this conversation, I learned that my ex-girlfriend had been accepted into a medical grant study sponsored by the NIH. She lived on the NIH campus and received permanent disability payments while serving as some sort of guinea pig for MND and ALS treatments.

When we met at Tivoli's, she gave me a book entitled, *When the Hunter Calls* with a note inscribed to me by the author that read: "If all that matters is love, listen only to the words written on your heart." Reading this book, she had realized what a wonderful thing I had done by not trying to cover up my true feelings for her out of some misplaced guilt over her illness. The last thing she wanted was to build a relationship based on pity rather than love. She said that I was one of the only people she could trust. All she wanted

106

from me was a little of my time to share some thoughts and ideas she was putting into writing. She was documenting the progress of her disease and working with a medical practice group to produce a guide plan for living and dying with ALS. The only men in her life wore lab coats and only wanted to get close to her heart with a stethoscope.

She asked whether there were any women in my life and I told her about my dismal failure to get a date with Alice. She thought it was even funnier when she heard about Alice's friends always mysteriously showing up. As we finished our coffee, I agreed to see her whenever I could. She agreed to make any future meetings easy by meeting me in my company lobby, which was conveniently located over the entry to the Rosslyn Metro station. But the stairs were a problem. Her disease had progressed to the point that she was unstable going down stairs and whenever we exited the lobby, she wrapped her arms tightly around me to steady herself while stepping to the curb.

This was the woman that Alice's friend had seen a few times leaving with me after work. This was who Alice had been thinking about on her flight down to Baton Rouge. While waiting for her luggage, she had checked her office voice mail and found a message from me asking to meet me in the Heidelberg's bar after she checked in. I added that she could bring her friends.

A Night to Remember

When Alice stepped into the lounge, my eyes were firmly fixed on her. She looked radiant in a Carolina Herrera two-piece skirt suit. A small, silver lily was pinned to the narrow lapels of the jacket that hung loosely over a matching gray skirt with soft pleats that fell an inch below her knees. Her beige, Georgio Armani blouse was open at the neck. A pair of Via Spiga shoes were daintily strapped around her ankles. But something was different about the way she was dressed. I finally realized that she was bare legged. Till now, she had always worn patterned or colorful opaque tights that accented her clothing. I had seen her in white, in black with a subtle herringbone stitch and dark-patterned tights. But now she was bare legged. Although she was still conservatively dressed, her silky, bare legs gave her a seductive look.

Alice slid onto the bar stool beside me. She swiveled in my direction and asked what I was buying her. Something was different about her; whatever it was, I liked it. I ordered a Brooklyn for myself and a Dark and Stormy for my wonderful new friend. She flashed a hint of a smile as she apologized that none of her colleagues would be joining us. Would I finally have Alice to myself? I wondered what had changed.

As the bartender placed our glasses atop the gilded napkins, Alice picked up her drink and pulled her hotel room key from her side jacket pocket. She said that she wanted to change for dinner, which would be in one hour. She told me not to be late. I almost slipped from the barstool at this provocative announcement.

An hour consists of 3,600 seconds. I counted every one. Each one seemed to last a minute and each minute an hour. What would I say to her at dinner now that we would finally be alone? The bartender did not blink when I asked to dump the Brooklyn and make me a club soda. At the 57-minute mark, I walked into the restaurant. I was immediately escorted to Alice's table in a dim corner lit only by candlelight.

She had changed into a clingy, dark beige, Nina Ricci dress with matching sandals. That was when it struck me; she was perfect. The dress was perfect. I could see her every curve in her body. She looked like a perfect Rockette.

"Rockette," I whispered, though I didn't intend for Alice to hear me. She looked at me questioningly. Embarrassed, I repeated, "You look like a Rockette."

I explained that when I was sixteen, my folks had taken me to New York at Christmas time and we went to Radio City Music Hall. The Rockettes had entered the stage in a straight line, with the tallest on the left and the shortest on the right. Each one had been perfectly curved in the chest and hips. They wore red coats and trousers to resemble the nutcrackers. Each wore a white helmet with a white chin strap. White suspenders that ran across their slender bodies were accented with the gold buttons and braid. The high-waisted trousers were painted on their hips, which outlined the symmetry of the perfectly-shaped female form. Is it any wonder then that, as an impressionable sixteen-year old, I thought they were perfect?

In her dark beige dress, Alice looked like the perfect Rockette. And something else had changed. Alice grabbed my hand and entreated me with a flirtatious smile to sit beside her. She said comparing her to a Rockette was the most wonderful compliment she had ever received. But there was more. She reached into her Louis Vuitton bag and pulled out a book I had seen before: *When the Hunter Calls*. I finally began to understand.

"A friend of yours came by my office and said you had forgotten to take this gift," she said. "She asked me to bring it to you." Apparently, my former girlfriend had visited Alice after hearing me talk about her that day at Tivoli's. Alice had spent an hour with her. Now she knew there was no other woman.

I kissed Alice, not caring who might be watching. Over the next several days, in addition to work, we made time for getting to know each other better.

The Brooklyn Cocktail
Neighbor to the Manhattan, the Brooklyn is made with extra-dry vermouth rather than sweet vermouth. Add Bulleit Rye and a dash of Amaro (Ramazotti preferred). Shake over ice until thoroughly chilled. Serve in a martini or old-fashioned glass

109

2 oz. Bulleit Rye

1 oz. Extra-Dry Vermouth

½ oz. Ramazotti (if you're adventurous, add three
splashes Peychaud's bitters)

You Can't Go Home Again — Usually

My hands jumped at the explosive burst of an
eighteen-wheeler's air horn, jerking me back to the reality of
crossing the Mississippi River. Horns were blasting
everywhere. Alice reached across my arm and began to tap
the Fit's horn. Our tiny notes were quickly swallowed by all
the other road noise.

Halfway across the river, I noticed the sign noting
that the Mississippi was the widest and longest river in the
U.S. The ferry used to be the only way to cross it. At the
halfway point, ferry captains would pull the chain of the
brass steam horn, and the blasts would be heard on both sides
of the Mississippi. The message to all within hearing distance
was, 'No turning back.' The tradition continued even after
the first bridge replaced the ferry crossing in 1935. I smiled
at Alice and she blew me a kiss.

My iPhone flashed with a message. Alice sent it to
the Honda's screen. We both laughed when we read it. It was
confirmation from the Heidelberg Hotel. We would be
staying in the same hotel where we had shared our first kiss.

But our joy dissipated rapidly as I reminded Alice
that the Heidelberg was not a pet-friendly hotel. Alice
slightly curled one eyebrow and mouthed what sounded like
"un huh". She certainly was less perturbed than me over this
situation. After all, Munchie and Tuffy would not want to
spend the night without us. They were fond of king-sized
beds, soft sheets and oversized windows to look through after
a long day in the car. This called for a plan. I turned the
problem over to the queen of plan making. By the time we

110

exited the Huey P. Long Bridge and turned onto Lafayette Street for the Heidelberg Hotel, a reverse escape plan had been developed. A "reverse escape" involved sneaking into a place rather than out of it. I listened as Alice explained my role. This would not be the first time we had snuck two felines into a building that wasn't prepared for them.

Long ago, after our first week in Baton Rouge, Alice and I had returned to Washington, D.C. Within two weeks, she could tell that I had fallen in love with her. About a month later, we met at Mr. K's where I turned and told her I had something to say. Seeing it coming, she placed her index finger over my lips and asked me not to say it. I couldn't stop myself. At the bar at Mr. K's, I told Alice I was in love with her. She said it was just an infatuation, that it would pass. She said it was due to my fixation on her as a Rockette. I shook my head and continued to tell her how wrong she was. I felt my love for her every day. When we left Mr. K's, Alice crooked her finger at me. Although we had seen each other almost every night since we returned from Baton Rouge, we had parted each night for our respective apartments. Tonight, she was inviting me home with her.

Alice lived on the top floor of a six-story, low rise on P Street on Dupont Circle. At that time, Dupont Circle was gaining national attention as the Capitol City's version of a Haight-Ashbury. The Halloween tradition of adult men tricked out in women's skirts and high heels racing eight blocks down Connecticut Avenue had already morphed from defiantly outrageous to only mildly unusual. The gay scene in D.C. had not yet been blunted by the AIDS epidemic, and Dupont Circle, with its fountains, benches and outdoor exhibits, was the spot for illicit assignations between the openly gay residents and the politicians and statesmen still in the closet. Sunny days found Dupont Circle filled with chess wizards looking for a challenge or trying to make a few bucks by playing five people at once. Tourists continuously popped up into the circle from the Metro with the longest escalator in the city. This ride from the train's platform to the street was so long that tourists could start and finish reading Walt Whitman's entire poem, *The Wound Dresser*, that was inscribed on the granite walls.

Dupont Circle was also the home of Kramer's Books, which included a full-service restaurant with patio dining and two floors of books featuring authors famous and not-so-famous. Next door was Melody Records. This was the center of the city's vinyl scene. If a song had ever been pressed on vinyl, it could be found at Melody Records. The store employed a professional cadre of musicologists who toiled by day selling Coltrane and Thelonious Monk for $4.99 and moonlighted as musicians at the city's underground bars and clubs. Melody was my favorite place to spend a Saturday afternoon. I couldn't think of a better place for Alice to have an apartment than on Dupont Circle.

When we arrived at her apartment, Alice handed me a cold bottle of chardonnay. I fished a corkscrew from the utensil drawer and removed the cork from a bottle of *Sonoma Cutrer Les Pierres*. My wine choices typically had a price tag with only one digit in front of the decimal point, unlike the one I was now opening. Alice clearly had good taste and the paycheck to satisfy it.

There was also familiar music pulsing in the air. I recognized the sounds of "*Ay, Tite Fille*" with a Zydeco beat. Alice had found a copy of it at Melody. It was the Zydeco tune we had first heard on a hot, humid night in Baton Rouge. Alice took the wine glass from my hand, and I moved to inspect the turntable spinning the vinyl. My eyebrows went up at the sight of a Marantz 6370Q. I expressed my admiration for her choice. My discs still spun on a Technics model I had bought from a Chicago neighbor before moving to D.C.

I told Alice I was holding out for a new, high-tech music gadget that the rumor mill said was imminent. An article in Variety touted a Japanese hand-held device with a cassette player and earphones that reproduced sound with maximum fidelity. The little hi-fi in your hand was finally coming to the U.S. after a three-year wait.

Alice reached up to the shelves above her turntable and pulled down a small, palm-sized cassette player. She stuck it in my hand. As I plugged in the earphones and pressed Play, my head filled with the perfectly reproduced vocals and instruments of Elton John's remake of The Beatles' "Lucy in the Sky with Diamonds". This was the version Elton had produced with an unknown artist named Winston O'Boogie who played guitar and provided backup vocals. The unknown artist was actually John Lennon. Lennon had worked with Elton John and made this cut in the midst of his Lost Weekend phase. During this Lost Weekend, the famous Beatle had spent eighteen months apart from Yoko and traveled the U.S., dropping in unexpectedly to accompany musical friends like Elton John. When he recorded the version with Elton John, he had insisted on playing incognito; Elton John obliged by identifying his guitar player as Dr. Winston O'Boogie in the liner notes. During Elton John's Thanksgiving tour at Madison Square Garden, John Lennon had hopped up on the stage in an unannounced appearance. I was sitting in the cheap seats. As Elton John took the microphone and revealed O'Boogie's real identity, the crowd went wild.

"I was there!" I exclaimed. "I was in Madison Square Garden the night that Lennon showed up to sing with Elton."

Alice smiled and whispered, "So was I."

These memories were rumbling around my head as I listened to Elton John and Lennon on this amazing gadget called a "Walkman" that Alice had so nonchalantly plucked from the shelf. When I finally remembered where I was, Alice was grinning. She clearly knew the effect this little electronic music player had on first-time listeners. I pulled out the earphones and told Alice I was impressed. She asked if I was impressed more by the Walkman or the choice of music.

"You mean the Zydeco tune on the Marantz?" I asked, pretending not to understand that she was asking if I was impressed that she owned one of the hi-tech musical gadgets I coveted.

She meant the music on the Walkman. "But Zydeco will always be our sound," she said, referring to our first Cajun dinner together in Baton Rouge.

We sat listening to more Zydeco with empty wine glasses on the table and our shoes scattered on the floor.

"We need to be together all the time," I blurted out.

"That would be a mistake," Alice replied. She insisted that my feelings were fleeting and that I would come to my senses soon.

When I pressed her about her feelings toward me, she smiled and said, "I am growing fonder of you."

"Fonder?" I shot back. "What does that mean?"

She just laughed and said, "Time will tell. You have to learn patience."

I was frustrated and about to put my shoes on and excuse myself when Alice did that finger-on-my-lips thing. She asked me to follow her down the hallway to the closed bedroom door. She told me that there was something I needed to know before we went any further.

She turned the handle on the door and slowly pushed it open. Light spilled across the room from overhead and bedside lamps. Sprawled out on the duvet were the two largest cats I had ever seen. LeRoy was a Sylvester cat in black-and-white tuxedo markings with white socks and a white blaze on his chest. He could have been chasing Tweetie in a cartoon. Lying beside LeRoy was Evie Mae. When the movie, *Alice in Wonderland*, had been shot, someone must have used Evie Mae to cast the Cheshire cat. I could almost see smoke rings rising from her head.

114

I looked at Sylvester and the Cheshire cat, and they looked back at me. Alice put her hand on my side and said that these were her babies and wherever she slept, they slept. That meant alongside or on top of her in bed. If I was okay with that, I was welcome to stay.

"Wow," was the only word I could manage as I sat on the edge of the bed. "I love cats!" I shouted and meant it. At least I intended to start loving them, I thought silently as Alice snuggled up beside me.

No Cats Allowed

We spent several weeks moving between my place and Alice's, which left me more and more dissatisfied with our situation. But Alice refused to commit. She continued to hold back from being in love with me like I was with her. No matter how many times I asked her to move in with me, she kept saying, "No. Too soon." Or she said "she couldn't break her lease, or that the weather wasn't right for a move." She always had an excuse to keep from making the commitment I wanted from her.

One night at Mr. K's, I pressed for a legitimate reason for not moving in with me immediately. I could see that she was conjuring excuses, but I had come prepared. As the bartender set our drinks upon the bar, he made a big scene over pouring Alice's drink. On cue, he knocked over Alice's glass. There, among the cubes of ice, was a diamond ring. It was my mother's engagement ring that had been fitted with her tiny pre-war solitaire diamond.

I picked up the ring, and got down on one knee. I looked up at Alice sitting on the stool above me and asked her to marry me. The bar was filled with early diners, and they applauded. Even the bartender clapped.

Alice's response froze the audience. She took the ring from my hand and crooked her finger for me to stand up. She plopped the ring into my jacket pocket and said, "I can't say

115

yes right now, but I'm not saying no. Please save the ring for later."

I sat down in disbelief. The bartender squirmed away to the far end of the bar, but Alice had more to say. She took my face in both hands, gently kissed me and whispered that even though she could not say yes to the ring, she would move in with me.

I was confused and a little stunned, but happy as well. The bar guests wondered why I was hugging and kissing the girl who just turned down my marriage proposal. We finished our drinks and left the bar, hand in hand, to the most perplexed looks imaginable on the faces of Mr. K's bar patrons.

This led to our first "reverse escape" situation. Alice had finally agreed to move in with me, but my condo building was not pet friendly. In fact, it was so 'un-pet friendly' that having an unauthorized pet was cause for eviction. But Alice had a plan designed to minimize the risk of discovery.

I had told Alice even though the bad news was my condo association did not allow pets there was also good news. The good news was that we didn't need to be concerned with the kitties being discovered once they moved in. No one could enter my place without my consent since it was not a rental. Although the homeowners' association that ran the building had a firm "no pets" policy, unless someone learned of their presence and turned us in, the kitties could live with us undetected. Our only concern was getting the kitties into the condo without being discovered. Alice had a simple plan. The condo had a freight elevator that was available for use with a tenant key. We would transport LeRoy and Evie Mae in two, large fabric-sided suitcases. The covered parking lot provided easy access to the elevator. We would drive to the entry door where I would load the 'suitcases' on to the luggage dolly, roll the dolly into the elevator, press floor number ten, and one minute later we would roll into our condo.

Everything went like clockwork up to the point of finding the luggage dolly. Alice had persuaded LeRoy and Evie Mae to get into the carriers without incident. She left the last two inches of the bags unzipped so the kitties could peer through the small opening and see Mom. She also threw a lightweight sweater over each carrier to help disguise the contents. When I returned without the luggage dolly, we decided to hand-carry the pet carriers; Alice took the one holding Evie Mae, and I carried the one with LeRoy.

Grinning at our cleverness, we rolled the carriers down the empty hallway toward the elevator doors. What we hadn't counted on was LeRoy tiring of the game and yowling. His sound grew louder as I approached the elevator. The steel doors opened, we rolled our two feline charges in, and pressed floor number ten. As the elevator began moving. we started to congratulate each other. Then the elevator stopped unexpectedly on the first floor where the main lobby and concierge were located. By this point, LeRoy was very unhappy. As two middle-aged maintenance men in blue work shirts entered the elevator, Alice began to speak in a very loud voice to cover up LeRoy's howls, completely ignoring the two maintenance men who had stopped their conversations when Alice began almost shouting about a movie we had seen the night before. I caught on to the ruse and began shouting back at Alice from six inches away, but it was no use. The louder we spoke, the louder LeRoy yowled until the elevator finally stopped at the sixth floor. The two maintenance men stepped out, and one turned back and said not to worry, that they wouldn't tell. We laughed so hard with relief that LeRoy stopped yowling to listen to us. As it turns out, many of the condo owners were opposed to the "no pets" policy and cheating was rampant. I told Alice it had been a good plan but that I hoped we would never need to use it again.

Now it was 35 years later at the Heidelberg Hotel and were about to use the 'reverse escape' plan, again. Step one called for me to conduct reconnaissance in the main lobby. My survey confirmed the only entrance was through the glass doors in front. We would need to negotiate two steps, open the doors and walk directly in front of the check-in desk, in clear sight of the bell stand and the concierge. I was to handle the check in while Alice waited till the last possible moment to get the cats into their carriers. I would firmly but politely reject the offer of help with our luggage and instead meet Alice at the Fit. We would leave our own bags and any evidence of traveling with cats (such as litter boxes) in the Fit for later transport. Alice would pull the wheeled cat carrier with Munchie stowed inside while I dragged the one housing Tuffy. We would have to pull the kitties' domiciles carefully enough up the two steps without alerting the charges to our surreptitiously intended actions and carefully guide the carriers through the glass doors without crashing into any pillars and generally trying to be invisible. The plan accounted for interference from a bellhop at this point. I would slip ten bucks into the bellhop's hand and ask him to keep an eye on the Fit, which I had intentionally left unlocked. Alice and I would slide our charges to the elevators and be out of the danger zone.

Although our plan did not work perfectly when we tried it with LeRoy and my condo, I still thought it could work at the Heidelberg. I commended Alice on her critical thinking that accounted for most contingencies. I wasn't clear on the penalties for cat smuggling in Baton Rouge and preferred to stay that way.

By the time I had executed my check-in role and returned to the Fit, the plan had begun to unravel. Tuffy took to the new game quite well. She hopped into the open travel case, and snuggled flat on the bottom without making a sound. Munchie, on the other hand, was not as complacent about traveling in a wheeled carrier as LeRoy had been.

118

No sooner did Alice zip the travel case shut than Munchie began a nightmarish yowling. Perturbed by the yowling cat-in-the-bag situation, I turned to Alice for guidance. She insisted that everything would be fine; we just had to see it through.

I pulled the Tuffy-loaded bag out of the Fit while Alice attempted the same with Munchie. Instead of dragging our rolling-critter homes up the two steps leading to the front door, we tried to arm-swing them over the steps. Instead, we swung the bags into each other, which startled the somnambulant Tuffy into a caterwaul equal to the yowl coming from Munchie. Perhaps it was the heat and humidity but more likely it was the fear of being caught cat smuggling that instantly drenched my face and hands in perspiration.

I hesitated to open the glass door knowing how the disturbing noises coming from our bags would reverberate in the lobby. Tucking a ten-dollar bill between my fingers, I proceeded to stroll into the lobby followed by Alice who stared at the ceiling in feigned ignorance of the screeching and caterwauling that bounced off the marble floors and into every ear in the lobby.

My worst fears were confirmed as the immaculately dressed young woman who had checked me in cocked her head in response to the cat noise. She held up her hand to stop us and almost slipped in her rush to block us from getting onto an elevator.

Alice and I turned toward each other and shrugged. We had been caught 'cat handed.' Sweat now ran in salty rivulets down the back of my neck, but Alice displayed no physical sign of guilt over our reprehensible behavior. Instead, she handed off Munchie's bag to me, and extracted her wallet from the Fendi bag slung over her shoulder.

As nonchalantly as if she were asking for ketchup, she extended her credit card to the young woman and asked her to please charge the pet fees to a separate bill. Stunned, I watched the receptionist ask if we had one cat or two; the fee was $75 each per night. Alice answered, "Two," and said she would retrieve the card when she returned downstairs for the luggage.

I kept my silence until we were safely on the elevator. "What just happened?" Hadn't Alice told me that the Heidelberg wasn't pet friendly?

"Oh, it's only 'not pet friendly' to dogs. We wouldn't stay here if the kitties weren't welcome."

"I thought we had to sneak them in," I said, still confused over our unnecessary act of deception.

"I thought it would be fun watching you go through the sneaky-cat contortions. And it was even better than I imagined. Do you forgive me?"

I stared in quiet admiration at my wife. Before I could answer, she said, "You're really sweating a lot. Maybe you should take a short nap."

Chapter 7: Dinner with the King

"No matter how hard you try to teach your cat general relativity, you are going to fail". B. Green, physicist

    With only the one night available for exotic dining in Baton Rouge, I sat quietly as Alice booted up her Apple Air and started the OpenTable app to find a spot open on Sundays. Every name she entered into the app came back with the same information: closed. I let this continue for about five minutes, pretending to be totally disinterested in her progress. After our just-completed cat-smuggling escapade, I was not going to be easily baited by Alice a second time in the same day. I knew Alice was checking one and only one restaurant and it was open seven days a week and had been open seven days a week for the past thirty-five years. I patiently waited for her to make her move. Finally, with a mischievous smile, she turned to me and said that every dining spot in Baton Rouge was closed – except for one. Together, we shouted, "Ralph and Kacoo's."

    Why had there even been a question. Of course, after a 35-year absence, we had to return to "our" restaurant. We had first discovered it on the second night of our long-ago client meetings in Baton Rouge. It was the night after Alice agreed that she was my Rockette girl. I wanted her all to myself, and we ensured our privacy in a tiny booth in a small restaurant off the main highway to New Orleans. Back then, we had chosen Ralph and Kacoo's partly because it was located outside of town and partly because it was so new that our Heidelberg concierge had never heard of it. We wanted to go somewhere unknown to ensure that we would not bump into any of Alice's colleagues.

Ralph and Kacoo's

As Alice sat the carriers in the back seat of the Fit I asked her if she thought the menu had changed over the past three decades. As we made the first turn from Lafayette Street it was clear that everything else had changed. None of the buildings or streets were recognizable as the Hondalink guided us along a totally transformed landscape. Thirty-five years ago, Alice and I had made the short trek using a paper road map for guidance. There had been no landmarks along the way. Now we were driving down the same highway but with two cats on our laps already purring contentedly. I told Alice that the landscape had been transformed from Mel Gibson's wasteland in *Mad Max* to Bruce Willis' glass and chrome futuristic cityscape of *The 5th Element*. The few, beat-up, shanty-style houses, auto junkyards and scrap metal yards that use to warn the traveler he was leaving Baton Rouge had been upgraded. We were driving in a corridor of 21st Century modernity. Along both sides of the highway were a continuous chain of apartment complexes with swimming pools and exercise rooms. LSU enrollment had expanded housing demand into the countryside. Class A commercial office space created business opportunities for the adjoining strip malls with nail salons and Big Lots stores.

Suddenly the Hondalink's friendly female British navigator alerted us to our Bluebonnet Blvd. turnoff, and we realized the truth of Thomas Wolfe's comment that "you can't go home again." We had arrived at our destination. It was barely recognizable from the past. Thirty-five years ago Alice and I pulled up in the dark to see a hand-lettered sign perched on the top of a desk-size wooden crayfish with the words "Ralph and Kacoo's" stenciled in white epoxy. It had been the third week of the grand opening and the chefs and owners had taken the rambling, 19th century, U-shaped farmhouse sitting on the edge of the Baton Rouge bayou in its 'as is' state.

A Coleman lantern hanging above the welcoming crayfish-shaped sign provided the only exterior light. A tin-roofed porch draped the entire U-shaped structure like the bill of a Houston Astros baseball cap. Sparingly placed under the sloping roof was a long row of rocking chairs. Under the center of the veranda roof was a double-framed door of solid wood with the words, 'Eats and More' carved into the top lintel. On each side of the door sat a children's bouncing board that was long enough to handle half a dozen bored kids waiting for their family's number to be called. The rocking chairs were empty. No kids were jumping on the bouncing board. We grimaced at the thought that the restaurant might be closed or worse yet we would be the only diners. Our concerns melted away as we entered the rambling clapboard building to the Zydeco notes of an accordion. We had passed from the moonless, black night into a cozy and softly lit Cajun oasis.

I still remembered how the cracked oaken door opened directly into a dining area that had been recently renovated. There were booths along three walls and a center bar with a donut-shaped hole from which the bartender could take orders from a 360 degree perspective. The refinished floors were stained with a clear lacquer that accented the cracks and grooves that had been weathered by 100 years of Louisiana storms.

Kitchen access was through a swinging wooden door that stood beside the last booth on the far wall. It was coated in rich maroon leather with firmly padded seats and backs. A marine lamp hung over each booth with a low-wattage bulb that spilled a warm circle of light onto the parchment-covered tabletops. A lone waiter dressed in a white apron passed umbrella drinks to the only other couple in the restaurant.

Inside the donut hole of the bar stood a bartender whose girth almost matched his height. We could not hold back our smiles as he noted our entrance with a drawling

Cajun patois so thick that we could only guess he said, "Welcome to Ralph and Kacoo's". I pointed to the middle booth on the far wall, and he nodded.

Seated on a short, round, piano stool beside our booth was an ancient relic dressed in a short-sleeved buttoned-up polyester shirt that was stuffed halfway into baggy brown trousers. They were held up on his scrawny shoulders by a pair of leather-braided suspenders matching those worn by partners at Alice's firm. He leaned back precariously, his weight counterbalanced by the full-sized, piano-key accordion on his lap.

Notes bounced from his squeezebox, and a laptop-sized Moog synthesizer cranked out guitar, fiddle and sax rhythms. The jazz-like arrangement of the rhythm and blues blended with his live accordion in a lively dance style. We slid into our booth opposite the musician and faced each other while holding hands. Alice whispered, "I love this place already." So did I.

As we shifted to better take in all the sounds of our entertainment, I noticed the name printed in capital letters across the accordion's fingerboard. We were being treated to the music of the King of Zydeco, himself: Mr. Clifton Chenier.

Dining with Pictures

The menu had changed since our first visit. For one thing, back then Ralph and Kacoo's had no menus. The lone waiter on hand that night had approached us with a clothespin snapped onto a handful of Polaroid pictures of different dishes. He had pulled the photos from the clothespin and handed the makeshift menu over to Alice. For ten minutes, Alice and I had stared at over a dozen photos showing a selection of appetizers, soups, salads and entrees.

The *Atchafalaya Plate* featured a grilled Gulf redfish with a golden edge, topped with an etouffee of delicately

124

fried crayfish tails topped by a roux. A close-up of the *Mahimahi Bourbon Street* practically jumped onto our plates with its tender, white mahi fish oozing zesty Vieux Carre sauce that was poured over the topping of garlic-infused sautéed shrimp.

My eyes and mouth could not resist ordering *The Ruby*. The waiter brought out a covered dish and deftly revealed the house-broiled filet of black drum. He slid it, smoking, onto my plate. Piled high and spilling over the filet was a potato-sized scoop of lump crab dressing, still smoldering from its stint in the Dutch oven. The waiter uncapped a china butter bowl and proceeded to drizzle a warm stream of *Ralph's Vieux Carre Sauce* over the dressing.

Alice found the photo of the *St. Charles* irresistible and was eager to try the lump crab dressing. The *St. Charles* arrived fully plated, and you could almost see the handcrafted care given to the dish. Butterflied and stuffed with crabmeat dressing, the golden-tipped shrimp indicated a chef who paid attention to his broiler. After setting the *St. Charles* before Alice, the waiter spooned out two heaping tablespoons of freshly made hollandaise sauce, and smoothed it over the dressing. Along with our entrees, the waiter served up two palm-sized bowls containing our sides of Cajun rice and steamed vegetables.

Ralph and Kacoo's had opened without a liquor license, so I was surprised to see the rotund bartender with a bottle of red petit syrah in one hand and a very nice albariño white in the other. Alice chose the white to pair with her hollandaise and shrimp, and I could almost taste the syrah swimming with the Vieux Carre sauce.

"Compliments of the house, gratis" he said, pronouncing it "graaaahtissse," as he poured a double portion of each wine into our empty glasses beside our plates. Apparently, the lack of a liquor license did not prevent Ralph from offering free wine to his dinner guests.

125

Before tasting these alluring dishes, we lifted our glasses to the man named Clifton Chenier and gestured to him to slide over and join us for a drink. Alice tipped a portion of her white wine into another empty glass and held it out to the musician. We introduced ourselves to Mr. Chenier, and the three of us toasted Louisiana living. Alice offered him a side plate filled with a piece of my black drum and Alice's *St. Charles Shrimp*. Mr. Chenier accepted it all as naturally as if he sat down with his accordion every day next to the dinner guests to share their meal. It seemed pretty natural to Alice and me, too.

I asked our new friend what folks around the area called his style of music. He leaned back with one hand around the wine glass and the other slightly pressing two of the accordion black keys to make a too-woo sound.

Smiling broadly, he asked, "Have folks where you come from ever heard of Zydeco?"

Alice and I both shook our heads blankly.

He asked if we had heard of a group called the Red Hot Louisiana Band. Again, we had to admit ignorance. He suggested that he could give us a taste of what we had heard while walking in the restaurant door. Ten seconds into his performance, Alice and I were both nodding. We were familiar with the music and the beat.

I was the first to say, "Jack Nicholson in *One Flew Over the Cuckoo's Nest.*" Jack had led his asylum mates in an escape adventure during which the inmates danced in the getaway bus aisles to lively New Orleans jazz punctuated with accordion polka notes.

Clifton Chenier grinned widely, nodded and said, "The tune in that movie is *"Ay, Tite Fille – Hey, Little Girl."* It was Clifton's first 45-rpm hit, and he had given permission for it to be used in the movie. Alice wanted to know more about the Red Hot Louisiana Band. Clifton had taken the band on the road for a six-month tour hitting a lot of dance venues scattered throughout the Gulf Coast. His audience

126

was made up mostly of country crossover listeners who enjoyed two-stepping to Clifton Chenier's bouncy tunes as much as they did line dancing to *Cotton-Eyed Joe*. Clifton's brothers made up the rest of the band, along with pickup jazz drummers they found along the tour. His brother, Cleveland, was the washboard player, and his half-brother, John Hart, kept the music jumping with a tenor sax. All three had tired of the overnight touring and after six months, the brothers had interrupted the tour and returned home for the summer. Clifton performed as a one-man Zydeco band at Ralph and Kacoo's out of friendship with the man who had backed him to produce his first vinyl record: Ralph, of Ralph and Kacoo's.

Ralph was a fifth-generation member of an Acadian family that had relocated to Louisiana from Nova Scotia in the late 18th century. He had been one of the first to recognize the unique sound that Clifton had created by elevating the Creole fiddle to second place next to the accordion in this new music genre.

Convinced of Clifton's talent, Ralph had paid for Clifton's studio time to get the '*Ay, Tite Fille*' 45 rpm produced, and Clifton returned the favor by performing. It was Clifton's offer to help with the entertainment that had encouraged Ralph to open Kacoo's outside of town, next to the bayou, without waiting for a liquor license that would take three months to receive.

Ralph was already known among locals for the best Creole-style cooking in the state. His marketing plan was to grow a customer base by offering free wine with outstanding food while listening to locally inspired music. Clifton had agreed to spend Saturdays and Sundays providing the music until his friend, Ralph, got his restaurant off the ground.

Clifton pushed back from our table and played a few more of his favorite Zydeco tunes for us. Even though we could not understand any of his husky-throated French/Cajun lyrics, his expressions told the story. As we finished our dinners, the waiter stopped by to ask if there was anything else he could offer, such as one of Ralph's specialty desserts.

I answered, "The one thing we would like is the recipe for the Vieux Carre Meuniere sauce." He smiled and disappeared into the kitchen. Moments later he returned and handed Alice a napkin with the recipe scrawled in dark blue ink. We may have been some of Ralph's first diners but I did not doubt that his free wine, exceptional cooking and local music would soon bring in the customers.

Ralph's Vieux Carre Sauce

6 tbsp. unsalted butter (_-inch diced at room temp., divided)
1 tbsp. flour
1 cup clam juice
¼ cup Worcestershire sauce
1 tsp. Creole seasoning (Tony Chachere's or similar)
1 clove garlic, minced
1 12-inch French roll, split

To make the Meuniere sauce, preheat a small sauté pan over medium heat, add two tbsp. of softened butter (reserve remaining butter to finish the sauce), and all the flour to the pan. Stir with a whisk for one minute to create a blond roux. Slowly add the clam juice, whisking constantly. Stir in the Worcestershire sauce, Creole seasoning, and garlic. Turn off heat and fold in remaining butter.

Clifton's Zydeco

After more than a thirty-year absence we had arrived on a Sunday evening to dine at a spot where the only thing that had not changed was the water in the bayou. The patched and rambling farm house was now a two-story, U-shaped façade of orange-stained stucco and wooden siding. The building sprawled in the center of a parking lot that accommodated more than 500 cars. Atop the roof was a bright yellow sign illuminated by a row of spotlights. Glowing neon-green in Cyrillic-like script, ten-foot tall letters spelled out "Ralph and Kacoo's". Only the shape of the restaurant was as it had once been.

Thirty years after our first Cajun dinner with Clifton we had returned to find a parking lot filled with hundreds of tourists listening to Bruno Mars' *UpTown Funk* blaring from the outdoor speakers. My first reaction had been to keep driving. I glanced at the GPS. It displayed a Popeye's Fried Chicken less than a mile down the road. Spicy chicken on a Sunday night made sense to me but Alice wagged her finger telling me *"no"*. I smiled back and said she was right – we had to do this. We parked, loaded the kitties into their carriers and headed into the crowded doorway of Ralph and Kacoo's.

We stood in line awaiting our turn for one of the half dozen hostesses. Alice gestured to the plaque above the door we had just entered. The sign noted that the occupancy of this restaurant was limited to 800. I shook my head remembering the only time I had been in a dining establishment that seated 800 people was in an Army 'mess hall' at Fort Leonard Wood, Missouri

Alice tugged me along to follow the hostess who led us to our table located on the far side of the cavernous restaurant. Although expecting the worst, I was greeted by the pleasant sounds of true Louisiana music. The place was filled with the jazzy sounds of a live band complete with accordion, sax, drums and what sounded like a washboard rub board. Our table was directly in front of the musicians who were arranged on a raised bandstand. Alice thought the location was perfect for a couple of diners lugging two cats. The noise of the band would certainly drown out any sounds from Munchie or Tuffy who were momentarily in invisible cat mode as they adjusted to the noise and clamor around them. Our hostess slapped two large plastic menus on the table and said that a waiter would be over immediately, if not sooner.

Alice perused the menus while I pushed back to get a better look at the band. Ever since our first dinner at Ralph and Kacoo's, we had maintained our interest in Zydeco. We'd been married for nearly fifteen years when we went to see *The Big Easy* starring Dennis Quaid and Ellen Barkin. For much of the American audience, this movie was their introduction to the unique sounds of a music genre created by a Louisiana accordion player named Clifton Chenier. Anyone who saw the movie would forever associate the vibrant notes of Zydeco when thinking about New Orleans.

I stared at the name of the band that was splayed across the drum set. Removing Alice's menu from her hand, I directed her attention to the band. We were listening to the *Red Hot Louisiana Band* led by CJ Chenier.

Alice shook her head. "It can't be the same Clifton J. Chenier from our past." Alice knew he was dead and buried in All Souls Cemetery. She had collected all of Clifton Chenier's music throughout the years since we had first met the musician in this very spot. We had followed his steady rise on the music charts, and watched him accept a Grammy on TV. She had also kept the newspaper notice of his death from complications of diabetes. The only difference I could make out was that the name on the drum set was CJ Chenier, not Clifton Chenier. I decided to find out more at the first break in the music sets. Alice grabbed the menu, pointed at the selections and said, "choose."

Two Cheniers

Looking around at the hundreds of other Sunday night diners hunkering down over the crayfish laden tables, it was obvious that Ralph's plan had exceeded his grandest expectations. The only thing that had changed was that the free wine was no longer free. No longer content with

130

Polaroid photos, Ralph offered up a menu selection only slightly shorter than Mr. K's Chinese in D.C. Never has one mahi-mahi filet been offered in so many styles and shapes. Alice flipped the menu over to show me that there were an equal number of dishes on the reverse side. I traced my finger down the offerings until I saw *The Ruby*. Alice seemed intent on finding something in the shrimp offerings; I guessed she was looking for the *St. Charles*. We smiled as the waiter took our beverage order and answered questions about the menu.

The Zydeco was drowning out most of what the waiter was saying, so we decided to point to the menu while mouthing, "Sparkling water and *The Ruby*." Alice pulled the waiter over to point to the *St. Charles* and asked for the hollandaise on the side. The waiter seemed relieved to have our order so quickly and asked if we had been there before.

"Yes," I nodded, "but it's been awhile."

He responded, "Welcome back!" and headed for the kitchen with our orders.

Alice and I leaned toward each other in order to be heard over the saxophone and accordion now belting out Zydeco dance tunes. Tuffy and Munchie had begun stirring, and Alice placed Munchie's carrier on her lap. Tuffy was content to stay in her carrier on the floor next to my chair as long as I periodically dangled one hand down into the carrier and stroked her head. Looking around at the dinner crowd, I had to be pleased for Ralph's success even if the intimacy that we had first experienced at the original Ralph's seemed lost forever.

I hoped that the intimacy was the only thing lost. We ordered the same dishes we had sampled on our first visit and we hoped that the chef's artistic touch would still be present. I wasn't putting a lot of stock in that hope and whispered to Alice that we would be fortunate if our dinners had not previously been frozen. She knew I wasn't joking as the prevalence of frozen shrimp and frozen fish filets was pretty

131

much a foregone conclusion when preparing meals for 800 people at a time. Fortunately, I was completely wrong.

Our waiter returned with our Pellegrino sparkling water within minutes of our order. He said, "Your dinners are in." He set a small egg timer on the table, already ticking down from 18 minutes to zero. A faint ticking sound began as the minute hand began to wind down.

Alice and I looked at each other with puzzlement. Our server said, "I guess y'all haven't been here since Ralph put in the dinner guarantee." He pointed to a plastic card sticking up from behind the salt and pepper rack. I pulled it out for a look. It promised that our dinner bill would be free if the egg timer went off before our orders arrived. We looked around and saw waiters who seemed to materialize from thin air carrying large platters that they unloaded throughout the restaurant. The waiter-to-table ratio was the best I had ever seen, even at a sit-down awards banquet where the meals were selected in advance. At Ralph and Kacoo's there were hundreds of choices, and some tables had as many as a dozen diners. How could Ralph make this guarantee? Ralph had enough waiters to deliver all the orders, but could the kitchen produce all these orders on time? I had to know, and Alice encouraged me to find out. As our egg timer showed one minute left, our waiter slid across the floor with our orders held high above his head.

He reached down and tapped the timer Off. With his right hand, he swiveled the platter onto our table and gently passed a china plate brimming with the *St. Charles* and another with *The Ruby*. No covered lids this time, but the presentation was perfect. I asked the waiter if I could see the kitchen.

"Of course," he said. "The tour galley is on the far wall and is always open to guests." I didn't know what a 'tour galley' was, but after dinner I planned to find out.

Alice was already into her crab dressing and waived her fork at me to take a bite of the beautiful mahi-mahi that was still smoking on *The Ruby*. After one bite, I was convinced that Ralph still had it. Somehow, he had grown an intimate and romantic dining spot into a gargantuan Creole restaurant capable of handling half the LSU student body at one sitting without losing the personal touch in the food.

The Red Hot Louisiana Band was playing when I went to visit the tour galley. Leaving Alice with our feline charges, I promised to return with a full report. Walking through the immense dining hall gave me a chance to scan a few of Ralph and Kacoo's other menu offerings. From the sound and looks of a few tables, it was clear that we were dining in a favorite spot for Louisiana crayfish. Splashes of red roux smeared on shirts and blouses were evidence of a sincere love of Creole cooking. Tables were weighed down with remains of the fried crawfish tails and lonely smidges of *Crawfish Etouffee* hanging on the edges of plates that were dotted with specs of basmati white rice.

Diners passed entrees back and forth which made it impossible to tell where the jambalaya started and the red beans and rice ended. The jambalaya was adrift with succulent pieces of chicken. It competed with hunks of sausage that could have been from Billeaud's. Most telling was the aroma wafting up from so many tables. My nose twitched at the spicy smell of smoked sausage that permeated the restaurant. Only five minutes had passed since I had finished my meal, but the rich, pungent smell of smoked sausage had me yearning for one more bite. Maybe this was Ralph's version of Las Vegas oxygen. (Several magazine writers had accused the Vegas casinos of pumping oxygen into casinos to keep the late-night gamblers fresh for the next roll of the dice. Maybe Ralph was pumping in that smoked-sausage smell to keep all the diners hungry for more. It certainly worked for me.)

The entry to the galley tour was through a set of double doors that opened into an enclosed space, like an airlock. I pushed through another set of double doors and

133

found myself in a long, brightly-lit hallway that ran ahead for what seemed like the length of a football field. One side of the hallway was a cinderblock wall that was plastered, floor to ceiling, with photos of kitchen staff preparing meal orders. The left side of the hallway was solid glass; it offered see-through windows from waist height up to the ceiling. A row of parents and kids were pressed up against the glass and stared down into the largest kitchen in Baton Rouge. It may have been the largest kitchen in Louisiana.

On the far wall downstairs, and running its entire length, were six- and eight-burner gas ranges interspersed with deep fryers and bread warming racks. Huge broilers the size of a Kelvinator freezer but with thick steel doors and glass fronts opened to show racks of metal pans filled with fresh pink shrimp and Gulf fish filets slowly broiling to a golden tint. Beside the double windows was a solid line of bins, each holding what the sign proclaimed as "*Fresh fish, twice a day, delivered dockside to Ralph's.*" Stainless steel bins were filled with three or four different sizes of Gulf shrimp. Other tubs and bins were marked with the species of fish they held. Flounder, mahi-mahi, amberjack, red snapper, tuna, sea bass, pompano and shark were iced down in separate bins where they awaited the filet knife. A dozen men and women smartly dressed in solid white, each sporting a chef's hat, scurried from broiler to range to center aisle plating each order as it finished cooking.

In the center of the kitchen was a built-in bar about fifteen-feet long and five-feet high with a glass-walled tank. It was a holding tank for a thousand pounds of live, swimming crayfish. That was just enough for one night at Ralph's. On each side of the tank stood two white-smocked cooks with minnow nets. As each new order for tails or platters popped up on a computer screen, a net would scoop a pound of jiggling crayfish out of the water and dump it into boiling cauldrons at each end of the center bar. Twenty-gallon pots sat on Bayou Banjo burners bubbling full tilt, while another white-clad cook scooped up the fully cooked crustaceans and divided them among platter and crawfish tail orders. Another chef stood waiting to prepare the 'tails-only' orders. With fingers flicking at the speed of light, the tails-only chef was popping crayfish tails at an eye-blurring rate. As stacks of crayfish tails piled up under his fingers, another chef swept them into bowls filled with the spicy dark roux that had been cooking on the ranges.

I had seen enough to answer Alice's question. Ralph had invested in the kitchen manpower and cooking equipment. His dinner timer and "free meal service guarantee" was all the incentive his chefs needed to keep the orders flowing.

Diners were still being seated as I made my way back to the table. The music had stopped, and Alice was sitting at the table with the Red Hot Louisiana Band's leader and accordion player. We shook hands. Alice introduced me to CJ Chenier, otherwise known as 'Jr.' This was the man who had taken over after Clifton Chenier's death in the late 80's. Alice told CJ about our meeting with the man we believed to be his father, Clifton, at the original Ralph and Kacoo's and how we still listened to '*Ay, Tite Fille*' on our 45rpm player. CJ laughed at the thought of using a 45-rpm player in the day and age of iTunes on the iPhone.

I noted that he didn't look a thing like his father Clifton. He said, "That has been a problem for me recently." He took after his mother, but his mother was not Clifton Chenier's legal wife. It seems that the Chenier sitting in front of us was actually a Thompson. His mother had been one of Clifton Chenier's paramours, and Clayton Joseph Thompson had not learned who his biological father was until he was fourteen-years old. CJ told us his father came to get him when he was a teenager and quickly saw that he had a talent for the accordion. CJ had been playing with his father in the band since he was twenty. He played with the Red Hot Louisiana Band right up until Clifton's death. After Clifton's

135

death, CJ took over the band and had been leading it as CJ Chenier the past twenty years.

"Now my father's blood relatives are suing me," explained CJ. He proceeded to tell us that his father, the original King of Zydeco had died without ever certifying that CJ was his biological son. Now twenty years after his father's death CJ was being sued. It seems his father's legal wife, Margaret Vital Chenier, had recently passed away, and the couple had no record of legal offspring. Relatives of Chenier's legal wife claimed in a lawsuit that Clifton Chenier, King of Zydeco, was biologically unable to have children, and therefore Clayton Joseph or CJ could not be his bastard son. The relatives were suing CJ to quit claiming "sonship" and enjoined him from using the name CJ Chenier and referring to himself as Chenier's son.

Alice interrupted to ask if he would be forced to leave the Red Hot Louisiana Band. CJ answered that it was unclear what his status would be if the relatives prevailed in the lawsuit. Since this man, the pretender to the throne, had been leading the band for the last twenty years, playing gigs and making popular albums, it wasn't clear why there was all the fuss over the name now. So, I asked. "What brought all this on so long after your father's death?"

"The money," he answered.

"What money?" I didn't see how there could be any inheritance issues after twenty years. CJ said it wasn't about Chenier's estate; it had to do with royalties. Chenier's music royalties had continued to flow after his death and were paid to his only beneficiary, his legal wife, Margaret Vital Chenier. Since Mrs. Chenier had passed away, her relatives wanted to make sure that they received the royalties, not Clayton Joseph Thompson, aka CJ Chenier.

I asked CJ if he was receiving any royalties from his 'father's' music; he said no. He had already disavowed any interest in the royalties.

136

I didn't see what anyone had to gain from the lawsuit. CJ retrieved from his accordion case a set of legal papers that had been filed in the Iberia District Court. He asked me to read them.

I said, "I'm not a lawyer but I know a little bit about royalties and royalty agreements." Alice told CJ that I had half a dozen issued U.S. patents related to controlling access to electronic data, such as music. Companies like Apple licensed these patents, and it involved all sorts of royalty agreements. As Alice was explaining this to CJ, it dawned on me that Alice had read my royalty agreements so many times that she probably understood a lot more about this topic than I did. I flipped through the documents CJ handed me and found the relevant words about the royalties in one subparagraph.

I asked CJ, "What has your attorney told you about these royalties?" His attorney advised him to settle the suit and not dispute it since he had already disavowed any royalties from the elder Chenier's music.

Alice saw me shake my head and she pulled the paper from my hand to read the same paragraph. She looked at the 'pretender' at our table and asked how many albums he and the Red Hot Louisiana Band had produced in the twenty years since his father's death. "Twelve," he answered. Two were still ranked among the top-twenty crossover hits, and the band won a Grammy for *Bayou Boogie*, which was still the top-selling Zydeco album.

"Any royalties?" she asked.

CJ slapped his thigh and said that was how he supported the band. The travel gigs never produced enough revenue to cover the expenses. Without those royalties, the Red Hot Louisiana Band would fold, and his bandmates would have to look for other work to support their families.

Alice and I stared at each other. This was an unusual breed of man. The unrecognized son of a musical genius who was a genius himself with a six-figure royalty income who

137

would rather spend his money keeping friends employed than retiring to a permanent Baton Rouge gig and living the good life. I could tell that Alice recognized the same.

I offered CJ my thoughts about the royalty paragraph. I explained that there were two ways to read it. One way was the way his attorney read the document. According to the attorney, in settling the lawsuit, the only thing CJ was agreeing to was to "henceforth receive no royalties from Clifton Chenier's music." That should not be an issue as CJ had already disavowed any interest in such payments.

But there was another interpretation that might stand up in a court of law. Under that reading, *all* royalties, including CJ's from his *own* music that he and his Red Hot Louisiana Band had produced, might be considered "derived from" *Clifton Chenier (now deceased) and the 'Red Hot Louisiana Band,'* not CJ Chenier and 'The Red Hot Louisiana Band.' This interpretation would attribute all the young CJ's current music royalties to his "father," Clifton. Settling could mean that CJ was disavowing all claims to his *own* royalties. In effect, CJ was about to be screwed, blued and tattooed. The color drained from CJ's cheeks, and for a moment I thought he might pass out.

Alice asked me what I thought could be done. CJ held onto the table and waited for my answer. I asked the waiter for a pen, and scribbled down a name and phone number from my iPhone contacts list. Isaac Goldman was one of the music industry's most celebrated and accomplished attorneys. He was an agent to many of the music industry's legends and Alice's and my dearest and closest friend. CJ looked at the name and asked if this was the same Isaac Goldman who had presented CJ with the Grammy award the previous year. It was; I thought Isaac would have no problem resolving CJ's royalty problem.

I was pretty certain that the lawsuit emphasized the injunction regarding the use of the name 'Chenier' purely as a smokescreen to divert attention away from the money paragraph about the royalties.

CJ looked at me and said, "It almost worked, too." He graciously thanked Alice and me. We paid for our dinners, picked up our kitties, waved a last goodbye to CJ and headed for the Fit.

Alice squeezed my arm and asked if I truly believed our friend Isaac could fix CJ's problem.

The solution seemed self-evident to me so I whispered to Alice, "Izzy Goldman will demand a DNA paternity test for CJ. His relatives will back off immediately rather than losing even their tenuous claims on the old man's royalties. Either way, CJ wins."

We stepped out from the loveliest aroma in the bayou, hopped into the Fit and headed back to the Heidelberg.

Chapter 8: Saints & Cats in NOLA

"Way down deep, we're all motivated by the same urges. Cats have the courage to live by them." Jim Davis, Garfield cartoonist

We returned to the Heidelberg Hotel from our dinner and chance meeting with CJ Chenier exhausted from the long day. It felt like a week had passed since we said goodbye to BigLig and headed for Beaumont and Baton Rouge. We needed a long, undisturbed sleep to refresh our minds and bodies for our first day in New Orleans.

Munchie and Tuffy were padding around the room, studying every chair leg and sofa cushion with their noses. While Alice soaked in the Jacuzzi, I was tucked between the Wamsutta sheets with my head on the pillows. I placed a handwritten note on Alice's pillow that read, "From the man in 319. You, dear Alice, will always be my Rockette girl – XXX." I drifted into a peaceful slumber with memories of another time floating in my head.

Cat Claws

My yell awoke Alice with a terrified start. I had jerked my knees beneath me, leaving me resting on my hands and knees. Alice's startled shout turned to hilarious laughter as she watched my sleep-addled brain process what had awoken me with a blood-curdling scream.

Munchie was preening at the foot of the bed, ignoring my distress and licking her face with one, tiny white-socked paw. Once again, the little terror had almost killed me with a cat-induced heart attack. While rolling onto my side during the night, a little warning bell rang somewhere deep in my brain. In my fatigued state, I had ignored the warning and failed to protect myself from the startling wake-up call that only a little tortoise-shell colored terror like Munchie could deliver. My six-foot-two-inch frame usually left my toes sticking off the end of the bed when I slept. My toes twitching under the sheet created an irresistible target for a hungry little tiger whose verbal supplications for the servant to arise and unlock the Fancy Feast were going unanswered. Unable to arouse me by walking on my back or licking my ear, Munchie had taken a more direct course of action. Standing on her rear legs, she unsheathed her needle-sharp claws and wacked my toes with both sets of weapons. The sharp sting of having the bottom of your toes lanced by eight, tiny needles can make a preacher cuss.

The only one to blame was myself. Munchie had done this before. As I fell asleep, my exhaustion had prevented me from pushing one of the pillows down to the foot of the bed to guard my toes from a possible Munchie attack.

Alice was still laughing as I twisted out of the sheets and followed Munchie over to her dish where the two cans of Fancy Feast sat unopened. It was futile to take out my pique on a fur ball. I threw a sharp glance over at my Rockette girl and announced we would be leaving in one hour.

Our departure was delayed while I took the Fit to find gas and a car wash. By the time I returned to the hotel, Alice had everything packed and ready for me to perform my stevedore routine. She was still surprised that I had developed a system for loading the car that ensured everything went into its proper place and still left room for the felines to roam.

We bid farewell to Room 319, happy to have relived a little of our past and reminded of how fortunate we were to still have one another after so many years. Alice was excited about New Orleans and looking forward to seeing the city again. I asked if she would mind a short detour to a nearby spot for a little history lesson.

"As long as the history lesson doesn't involve visiting the Huey Long State Capitol building or the LSU stadium, I wouldn't mind at all."

I laughed and assured Alice our visit would not involve either site. Alice and I had both seen enough of the Huey P. Long State Capital building during our travails of installing the state accounting system that had brought us together for the first time. Like me, Alice had been subjected to the mandatory tour that our Louisiana clients insisted on giving us when we first started the job. Taking in one tour with a client was a polite and agreeable consideration. My annoyance was due to the insistence of our overly effusive clients to repeat the tour every time we brought in a new programmer or accountant to help on the job.

After my third walkathon from the Speaker's Chamber to the Memorial Hall to see where the former Senator ex-Governor Huey P. Long, nicknamed The Kingfish, had been gunned down, I began to wonder if Louisiana natives took some perverse pleasure in the 'show and tell' related to the assassination. At the "exact spot" where Long was killed, an artist had inset into the tile floor a design of a sunburst within concentric circles. It probably hadn't been polite of me to point out that the spot looked as if it had been marked with a bullseye.

Baton Rouge Surprise

As we pulled away from the Heidelberg heading for my little history lesson I tapped the GPS with our next destination. The route ran from downtown into a precinct that had not completely recovered from the effects of the Great Depression. Even the GPS failed to show a couple of the side streets that had not seen a paving truck in 50 years. I pulled slowly to the end of two derelict warehouses that had broken windows on both the top and bottom floors. A chain-link fence with triple strands of rusty, barbed wire separated the empty lot at the end of the street from the warehouses. Alice looked at me, puzzled, as I announced that we had arrived. Alice pointed questioningly at the warehouses. I

142

shook my head; we were not heading for the warehouses but for an empty lot surrounded by a rusting chain link fence.

We locked the Fit and left the engine on with the air conditioning running for the kitties. We did this only when we were fairly close to the Fit so that we could return to the car quickly if necessary. In front of us was an open section of the fencing leading into an abandoned field. At one time, the chain-link fence had protected the jungle of vines and scrub pine from curiosity seekers or vagrants looking for a place to crash, but time had collapsed most of the fence, and it was barely visible through the thick layers of kudzu. Two well-trod paths had been pounded through the ground cover indicating that the once-restricted space had become a shortcut from one side of Florida Boulevard to 3rd Street.

Alice pulled me up short after a few steps. "I know what I'm doing," I assured her. She rolled her eyes, grabbed my arm and walked beside me as we approached a pile of junk, overgrown with plants, near the rear lot. The scrap heap of metal pilings and split lumber was barely visible under the vines. I stopped to give Alice a clear look at the metal sign that hung lopsided from a rusted rail.

She dropped her hands from my arm, and put her hands to her mouth. "Oh my God!" she said, staring in disbelief at the words on the sign: *The Wild Mouse*.

Seldom at a loss for words, Alice just pointed at the remains of the Wild Mouse amusement ride. Not just any Wild Mouse, but the first Wild Mouse ever built in the U.S.

The German Engineer, Franz Mack, had conceived of and built the first working model, complete with scaffolding, track and two Wild Mouse coaster cars, in the late 1950s in a little place near Frankfurt called Wittigen, Germany. Unable to secure expansion financing in Germany for his project, he had traveled to the U.S. looking for a financial benefactor. Most of Franz Mack's U.S. prospects were involved in the amusement trade. He had appointments with prospects from Coney Island, NY, to Fun Fair Park and Pontchartrain

Amusements in Baton Rouge. Franz Mack had sent detailed design drawings of his new invention, and included the black-and-white photos of the working prototype. Soon after arriving in New York, it became clear that his financial prospects were not interested in an unproven amusement-park ride and certainly not one available only in Germany. Without a working model in the U.S. to show potential investors, Franz Mack had been unsuccessful at convincing his U.S. prospects to invest in his plans. His last stop for fundraising would be in Baton Rouge where he intended to stay on his way to boarding the Princess Lutetia for his return to Hamburg.

As Franz Mack had never heard back from the Fun Fair Parks and Pontchartrain Amusements owner, he had no reason to think that a man named Sam Haynes would be interested in his project. He was more than surprised to arrive at Fun Fair Parks to discover a huge banner advertising the most exciting roller coaster in the U.S. Franz Mack went to see it for himself.

Instead of a wood-and-steel track with coaster cars, he found a tent and Sam Haynes who was selling five-dollar tickets for lifetime passes to ride the most exciting roller coaster in the U.S.; it was scheduled for delivery any day. Using the design documents and photos sent by Franz Mack, Sam Haynes, a creative and entrepreneurial LSU mechanical engineer, had constructed a perfectly matched 1:10 scale model out of cardboard and assembled it under his tent. With no more than a mural of his dream roller coaster, Haynes had already sold over 800 lifetime passes. The proceeds were enough to pay for the shipping and assembly of Franz Mack's Wild Mouse from Hamburg to Baton Rouge. The rusted remains of what had once been billed as *America's number one amusement ride* now lay in a jumbled heap, overgrown with Louisiana kudzu, in a forgotten warehouse lot in Baton Rouge.

144

When Alice took her eyes off the rusted Mouse, she said, "You remembered."

"Yes, I remembered." I thought that seeing the demise of the scariest ride in American amusement-park history would help Alice overcome her nightmares.

We had been married two years when Alice's infrequent, but not exactly rare, bad dreams began occurring often enough to wake us both. When she told me about her recurring dream of riding the Wild Mouse ride, I realized how terrified she was.

The Wild Mouse was frightening enough in real life. Franz Mack's invention included two design changes to the traditional roller coaster. First, he designed the cars to be much wider than the tracks. This gave riders the feeling of hanging over the edge of the rails. Second, he made the tracks narrow and shaped them with short, flat runs leading into sharp, almost 90-degree turns. The wide cars, narrow tracks and sharp turns fooled the passenger into thinking that the cars were about to fly off the rails. An intentionally wrecked Mouse car was stuck, nose first, into the ground to help seal the fear. I told Alice she wasn't the only one with nightmares.

In Alice's Wild Mouse nightmare, she is riding in a two-person car, but cannot see the face of the person riding with her. She is about to make the first sharp turn when the Wild Mouse starts its herky-jerky pull up the steep incline before dropping 50 feet to where the track flattens out. Lights from below illuminated the right-angle turn ahead. In her dream, Alice sees a break in the track at the far corner of the angle bend. She knows that instead of a sudden lurch to the right, the car will skid forward, sail into the air and crash to the ground below. Alice always wakes the moment the car flies off the track. She has been having this same dream since her one Wild Mouse ride in the sixth grade at Elitches Garden in Denver, Colorado. She had tried to cure herself by

145

riding various roller coaster rides at Virginia Beach, but those attempts only triggered her bad dreams.

"How did you find it?" she asked. I told her about my Dogpile search for interesting historical sites around Louisiana. One of the links was to a Pinterest site entitled *Things Remembered about Baton Rouge*. One photo was a shot of the empty lot with an arrow pointing to the location of the last remaining Wild Mouse car. I used Google Maps to identify the location in the photo. Once I knew the location of Fair Parks' Wild Mouse, I had surreptitiously included it as a potential visit for our trip. Just maybe, I thought, if Alice saw the rusted skeleton in the Wild Mouse cemetery it would put an end to her nightmares. Alice tapped the side of her temple to let me know that she appreciated my using the "old kidney" to help her, but she thought it was better left to a therapist. We waved goodbye to the Wild Mouse, walked back to our car and kitties, and set out for New Orleans.

Monteleone or Bust

Within minutes of their release from the carriers, Munchie had wrapped herself around the center console while Tuffy stretched out on the dash. They acted as though the luxury rooms awaiting them at the Monteleone were nothing to get excited about. Alice and I, on the other hand, were looking forward to our next destination. Returning to New Orleans for the first time in ten years was reason enough to be a little excited, but our booking into the Monteleone (a pet-friendly hotel) raised our anticipation a little higher. Though we hadn't previously stayed there, we had been in the lobby several times, having visited the city for business and pleasure at least ten times. It was one city we always managed to visit together. Even when we worked at different companies, if one of us had a conference or convention trip to New Orleans, the other would change their schedule to go along.

Our Hondalink displayed a birds-eye-view of our route from I-10 onto Canal Street and then onto the narrow, one-way streets of the French Quarter. Alice was busy coaxing the kitties into their carriers while I maneuvered the Fit into the three lanes of Canal Street from which I tried to turn onto Chartres Street. It ran one way in the wrong direction, and my British navigator kept repeating "Make the next left turn, make the next left turn..." There was no left turn to be made into the traffic coming toward me from Chartres Street.

I made my first mistake, deciding to pass Chartres Street and make the next left turn onto another one way that headed in the right direction. Then I made my next mistake. I shut off the voice of British navigator who kept admonishing me to "make a U turn." As the traffic light changed from green to orange, I swung the car in front of a city bus, a yellow taxi, and a pedi-bike, pretending not to hear the horn blasts and shouts and inched my way down Iberville.

The horn blasts panicked Munchie who jackknifed from Alice's lap into the rear compartment, leaving tiny holes from her claws in her chino pants. That was when I made my third mistake. Alice covered her mouth before I said those five fateful words that have plagued the male of the species for eons: "I know what I'm doing."

I thought I did, and I could have pulled it off had I not made one more error. Confused by the traffic and the ad hoc routing change, I calculated that the Monteleone was three blocks away, which would put the garage on my left before reaching Royal Street. But my routing change meant that we would reach Royal one block south of the Monteleone, not immediately adjacent to it. If only there had not been a municipal garage with the large block letters spelling out "GARAGE" on the very same corner where I expected to find the Monteleone garage, everything would have been okay. At the sight of the sign, I turned into the open entryway for the city garage rather than the hotel garage, and pulled up

to two parking attendants who stood in front of a large
electric fan.

The Great Cat Caper

Outside of the air-conditioned Honda Fit, the garage
temperature and humidity each registered in the nineties.
Exhaust fumes were being circulated with the oversized fan
that was stacked on a row of cinder blocks. The two
attendants strolled over to our car. I lowered the window just
a few inches to warn the men about our kitties, still running
loose in the car, while Alice went into capture mode. But the
heavyset man pulled open the door in a move that was clearly
meant to be polite and helpful, and Tuffy bounced her
oversized body across my lap and out the door before the
word 'STOP!' could clear my throat. The attendant and his
buddy backed up as I threw the door open and shouted,
"Follow that cat!"

Alice managed to lock Munchie in her carrier before
jumping onto the oil-stained garage floor to assist. Garage
staff sped out of their offices to help track Tuffy. Alice
shouted for me to take care of the car, check in at the
Monteleone and tuck Munchie into our king-sized room
while she stayed in the garage to retrieve Tuffy. In the noise
and confusion, the only thing I had learned was this was not
the Monteleone Hotel garage; that was one block over on
Bienville.

Twenty minutes after completing my assigned task, I
raced back on foot with an empty carrier, hoping that Alice
had been successful in the hunt. The administrative manager
of the garage reported that Alice and two attendants had
followed the distraught kitty up the ramp and were now
somewhere between the second and fifth levels. The manager
led me to an oversized fan-belt with steps running in a
vertical loop. Grabbing onto the belt and stepping on to the

slowly rising steps, I felt myself being lifted to a step-off space on the second floor.

Amazed that such an effective, but potentially deadly device could survive in a country where OSHA ruled supreme, I almost didn't notice the makeshift office in the back corner of the second level. What I did notice was the unmistakable aroma of cannabis drifting among the parked cars. As I approached the makeshift office equipped with two small chairs and a long extension cord for a TV, I could tell that the space had recently been occupied by a person or persons smoking a Bob Marley-sized, hand-rolled doobie, the remains of which were smoldering in a coffee tin on the floor. I was only glad that the smoker was not parking my car, and I took off up the ramp to find Alice and her helpers.

As soon as Tuffy had jumped from the Honda, a picture had popped into my head. I could see hundreds of cars parked on each floor with Alice and me crawling on our hands and knees with a flashlight, looking under each car to spot the terrified kitty. By the time I got to the fourth floor I could hear the voices of the searchers. All the overhead fluorescent lights were glowing, and Alice was, indeed, bobbing up and down between rows of cars while several garage helpers, also with flashlights, were doing the same from the other end. They had already searched the top floor without flushing out the feline. I wasn't sure where I could help.

I gave Alice a quick update on Munchie and took my place among the searchers. Alice passed me the flashlight. With all of us working in unison, we soon cleared the fourth and third floors and were back on the second level where I had started.

Suddenly, Alice stopped us all in our tracks, took the carrier from my hands and told us to be quiet. She sat down in the middle of the aisle and slowly pulled the carrier's zipper up and down. The zipping noise buzzed in the air and seemed to bounce off the wall. Alice used this trick whenever

149

she had trouble cajoling Tuffy into the carrier. Then, ever so faintly, I heard the tiny cry of our fat-bottomed girl. The zipper noise was the sound of safety. Alice held the carrier and walked softly toward the sound that was now coming from near the makeshift office. The helpers and I watched as Alice called our kitty's name and set the carrier beside the two chairs. Shortly, a black cloud slinked from the corner and poured itself into the carrier. Alice had done it again. Although my bare knees had been scraped bloody, and my cargo shorts looked like a mechanic's grease monkey had worn them, the cat caper was closed. Alice shot me the 'give the men a big tip' look, and I fished out a twenty-dollar bill that I gratefully handed over.

Ride the Carousel

Walking from the city garage gave me a good clear view of what the search had done to Alice. Her chinos were too damaged for even Goodwill. Her white blouse now matched her torn and stained pants, and her smudged cheeks and forehead reminded me of Kurt Russel's smoked and smudged fireman's face in the movie *Backdraft*. I suggested, tongue in cheek, that we not stop at the front desk and instead go straight to the room.

"Do ya think?" Then she put her free arm around me and said, "Thanks."

Our room was a cool oasis compared with our garage adventure. Alice set the carrier on the floor and unzipped it. Tuffy shook her head from side to side and stretched out in her new, safe place. Munchie had already disappeared behind the Samsung flat-screen TV and had safely wedged herself into the armoire console. I promised Alice a trip downstairs to the Carousel Bar as soon as we freshened up.

One half hour later, we were standing at the door of the Carousel, scrubbed and dressed in our summer whites. It was early in the day, and the bartender motioned us to take any open seat. On two previous trips to the city, we had been denied entry to the Carousel Bar due to the crush of thirsty customers. This time, we did not have to fight a crowd.

The Carousel Bar at the Monteleone is an actual carousel. Twenty-five stools are arranged around a circular bar. Overhead hangs a back-lit carousel canopy, complete with ornately decorated animals of exotic species. The bartenders are positioned in the center, and the round zinc bar top along with all 25 bar stools make a complete revolution every 15 minutes.

Bartenders at the Carousel are reportedly the highest-paid hospitality workers in the city. They deserve it. Serving over 600 beverages a day between 5:00 p.m. and 2:00 a.m. is only half the reason for the outstanding compensation. Keeping track of who ordered the Dark and Stormy versus the Sazerac while the patrons are constantly rotating is the challenge. Customers at the Carousel pay, on average, $12 for a house-specialty cocktail. The best way to keep them happy is to make sure they get what they ordered. Patrons have even been known to change barstools after ordering in a challenge match to see if the bartender can keep their orders straight. They can. I heard that some nights a single cash tip might be a Ben Franklin.

We sat down, and Alice did not hesitate when the bartender approached. Before the words left her lips, I knew she would order a Kentucky Mule. Alice loves bourbon. Before she had met me, she didn't know how to spell "bourbon." Now she could argue the taste merits of different brands with the bartender. "Pappy Van Winkle," she rattled off, looking for the bartender's expected wince.

At another bar, the bartender would just say, "Sorry, we don't carry that brand," and suggest a cheaper, wheat-based replacement like Rebel Yell. In an upscale bar like the Carousel, the wince was followed by the bartender offering to substitute Makers Mark, which was Alice's favorite behind Van Winkle.

"No Pappy's?" I asked with feigned incredulity over the absence of a single bottle of Pappy Van Winkle.

Without interrupting his measured pour of two ounces of the caramel-colored Makers Mark, the bartender chuckled and asked if I had heard about the robbery?

Taking the bartender's bait, Alice said, "What robbery?"

"Someone stole the entire years' worth of Pappy Van Winkle right out from under their noses up in Frankfort," answered the bartender.

"How did that happen?" I asked.

"They have no idea. So they say. But my money's on it being an inside job." I noted that the bartender's thick Southern accent plastered with a backwoods drawl didn't seem to fit his demeanor

"Why's that?" I asked.

The bartender pulled back a bit to eye me once more. When I asked if he was serious about a robbery, the bartender cast a piercing gaze at me. With his close-cropped head of snow-white hair, he could have been 60 or 80 years old. His face was smooth, and his pushed-up shirt-cuffs revealed stout forearms the shade of coffee with cream. His writs were wide and tapered down to thin, almost, delicate fingers. His gaze weighed me, measured me, and seemed to find me to his liking.

"So you really haven't heard about it?" he said again, setting down the bottle of Powell & Mahoney ginger beer that he was pouring into Alice's Kentucky Mule. This time, there was no hint of a drawl. I confirmed that I had not heard of this heinous crime against Van Winkle and added that I hoped it wouldn't affect my order for a case of Elmer T. Lee.

From the look of satisfaction on the bartender's face, it was clear my mention of Elmer T. Lee private-reserve bourbon had sealed the deal. He knew he had my respect. With those words, he stuck out his hand, introduced himself as Lincoln Stevens and said, "Let me welcome a true

152

bourbon man to town." With that, he held up the shiny copper mug as he garnished it with a slice of lime and pointed the mug over to his accessories board. Alice followed his direction and said, "Yes, please!" to the unspoken question of splashing in the Rose's Lime juice. I winked at Alice. We had come to the right spot.

Having ordered Kentucky Mules from a hundred different bartenders in over 30 states, Alice could now attest that at least two understood that a perfect Mule needed Powell & Mahoney ginger beer and a heavy splash of Rose's Lime juice to finish the drink. Lincoln knew this special touch, as did a bartender at the Four Seasons in Manhattan. Now comfortable we had found a new friend in New Orleans, I encouraged Lincoln to give us the rest of the story on the stolen Pappy Van Winkle.

Lincoln asked our source of information regarding Pappy's. I made a mental note of his question about "our source of information about Pappy" instead of the more common, "Where did you hear about Pappy?" I told him that Alice and I had discovered Pappy Van Winkle bourbon when we visited the Buffalo Trace Distillery during a stopover on our one and only visit to the Kentucky Derby. Lincoln interrupted and asked if we were Kentucky Derby aficionados or perhaps dilettantes at handicapping.

"Neither." I laughed. "We're cat lovers," I said. I told him, "We bet $20 on Alysheba and won 18:1. We just liked his colors. If we had known anything about horses, we would have bet on him to win the Preakness." I went on to say, "We used the Derby payout to buy two extra nights' lodging on the Bourbon Trail after leaving Louisville. Along the Trail, we tasted sour mash whiskey from the Bulleit Distillery and Evan Williams in Louisville, and from Buffalo Trace and Woodford in Frankfort, and Makers Mark and Jim Beam in Clermont." I told Lincoln that I learned that Jack Daniels might be the best-selling sour mash in the world but strictly speaking, it is not bourbon.

He laughed and said, "Most folks go to their graves not knowing that fact." On the Bourbon Trail, Alice and I learned all bourbons are sour mash because they are distilled from a minimum mash of 51% corn. That goes for Pappy, Elmer Lee, Makers Mark and Jack Daniels. But not all sour mash is bourbon, because, by law, to be labeled bourbon, the distilling must take place in Kentucky. Jack Daniels, as every bourbon drinker knows, is distilled in Lynchburg, Tennessee.

The other fact I learned was that a bottle of Pappy Van Winkle 20-Year Reserve sells for $250. That was almost how much Alice and I had won betting on Alysheba. We splurged and had bought a bottle of the Thirteen-Year Reserve for $80. After one sip, Alice said it was cheap at twice the price. Fortunately for our wallets, after tasting Pappy's, we visited the Makers Mark distillery in Loretto, Kentucky. Alice decided if she couldn't have Pappy, she would take Makers.

As I was telling Lincoln about our whiskey tour, he leaned in and asked Alice if anyone had explained to her why her choice of choosing Makers Mark as a substitute for Pappy Van Winkle was perfectly natural.

Lincoln said, "Most people know Pappy Van Winkle because it is expensive, not because of the flavor or taste. Some people can taste it some can't," he said. For those like Alice who could taste it, bourbon has one of three discrete flavors derived from the grains used in the mash. Some people can discriminate between these discrete flavor elements but most cannot.

My ears were picking up on Lincoln's use of words like "discrete" and "discriminate." I had also logged away his question about being "aficionados or dilettantes." I decided to listen a little closer to this unusual purveyor of bourbon.

Lincoln continued explaining that the law specified that all bourbon must use at least 51% corn. These days, all bourbons use 70% corn; the remainder consists of barley and rye, which are called flavoring grains. Traditional bourbons, like Wild Turkey use equal parts barley and rye, while spicy bourbons like Old Grand Dad or Woodford use more rye than barley. Makers Mark and Van Winkle use barley and wheat rather than barley and rye. The softer, sweeter taste of Pappy Van Winkle and Makers Mark result from the wheat. Lincoln called this distinctive taste the 'Van Winkle flavor spot.' Alice's flavor buds had detected the 'Van Winkle flavor spot' when she tasted Makers Mark. Even though they were completely different brands, Alice had correctly identified their common denominator, and associated Makers with its more expensive cousin, Pappy Van Winkle.

As Lincoln concluded our bourbon education, I jokingly said that I wished I had taken notes. He said, "Not necessary," and pulled from under the bar a slick little black-and-white brochure entitled, *Bourbon is More than Booze*. It was written by Lincoln Douglas Stevens, BS, MS, PhD, Professor Emeritus at Tulane University. That explained what I had picked up in his vocabulary. I wondered how many visitors to the Carousel Bar ever learn that this master of mixers was enjoying his retirement from the University serving up Kentucky Mules and Sazeracs.

The Carousel continued its steady rotation and carried Alice and me out of range from Lincoln. We took seats at one of the side tables beside the plate-glass windows overlooking Royal Street.

As soon as we sat down, I opened the menu card. Even in the dim light, the distinctive logo for Donald Link's Cochon Butcher stood out. Alice laughed. "Did you plan this?" she asked. I swore, truthfully, that until I saw the menu cards, I had no idea we could order from our hotel and have the food delivered to our table at the Carousel Bar.

Choosing our dining spots in New Orleans had been difficult. At the top of our list was the perennial restaurant-of-the-year winner: Herbsaint. This Donald Link Cajun bistro, cousin to Chef Link's Cochon Butcher restaurant, was the master chef's first dining spot and the place where Alice

155

and I discovered that there was more to New Orleans cooking than Emeril's.

It had been ages since my Rockette girl had dragged me off a streetcar named desire and into this classy, little white-table clothed bistro hidden under a porte-cochere on St. Charles Avenue. It was in the back room of Herbsaint with its ladder-back chairs and covered tables, that we broke our cherished vows to Emeril Lagasse and, as cheaters often do, guiltlessly indulged our sinful lust knowing that we were not the first to do so. Alice had taken the first bite of Donald Link's small plate of house made *Spaghetti with Guanciale and Fried-Poached Farm Egg*. Before she could spear a second taste my fork punctured the fried-poached egg that spilled its thick, orange yolk across the fried panko breadcrumbs and into the pasta.

Alice dabbed at a spot of lemony cream in the corner of her mouth as I forked the first bite of egg, spaghetti, and cream into mine. My eyes widened as the casing of smoky guanciale broke under my teeth, flavoring the bite with Donald Link's signature Cajun taste. Alice pushed her plate over to me, resisting the urge to eat the remainder of the delicious treat. I could only fork more of this divinely inspired Southern comfort into my mouth as the server delivered Alice's entrée: a *Banana Brown-Butter Tart with Fleur de sel Caramel*. Alice had ordered Herbsaint's signature dessert as her main course. When she ordered, the waiter did not blink an eye.

"Happens every night," he said as he scribbled down my order of *Beef Short Rib with Potato Rosti.*

Eulogy for a Cat

Sitting at the side table in the Carousel with nothing more than delicious memories on our plates, I asked Alice if she wanted to change our dinner plans and return to Herbsaint. She tapped the menu card from Cochon Butcher and said, "Don't change a thing." As much as we would have wanted to return for one more gastronomic delight, we would keep our engagement tonight at the almost secretive Gautreau's, housed somewhere deep in the Garden District. Tomorrow night, we would dine at a neighborhood favorite of James Carville's called Clancy's. Herbsaint would have to wait for our next trip. For today's lunch we elected to sample take out from Cochon.

The Cochon menu at the Carousel Bar features a few of Butcher's most popular offerings. On previous visits, we had followed our impulse to try something new and different, and the Pastrami Duck Sliders had met our expectations. My favorite was still *Butcher's Pork Belly with Mint and Cucumber* while Alice had fallen for Donald Link's clever ad for *Le Pig Mac*: two all-pork patties, special sauce, lettuce, cheese, pickle, onion on a sesame bun. With these yummy lunchtime choices in front of us Alice made an executive decision. Donald Link's *Muffuletta* was going to be our lunch. Alice reminded me that In all of our visits to New Orleans we had never once tried the city's namesake sandwich – neither of us had ever ordered the *Muffuletta*.

While we waited for our *Muffuletta*, I Googled to find the full story of the great Pappy Van Winkle bourbon robbery. Lincoln was right; it did appear to have been an inside job. I read Alice the news that an eighteen-wheeler carrying the entire season's production had disappeared in route from Frankfort to the Chicago distribution center. The White Freightliner had been hauling 700 cases of Pappy Van Winkle 20-Year Reserve. Upon arrival at the freight dock in Chicago, the metal seals across the doors were intact; no one had tampered with the cargo in route. But no one could explain how 8400 bottles of $200 dollar-per-bottle bourbon had vanished from inside the cardboard cases that were now filled with bottles of Dasani spring water. Liquor wholesalers from coast-to-coast were being asked to report any information that would lead to the arrest and conviction of

157

the perpetrators. I joked with Alice that a $1,000,000 reward, payable in cash or bottles of Pappy Van Winkle, was being offered. She laughed out loud.

Thirty minutes later, we split the *Muffuletta* in two and settled back in our wing chairs to enjoy the Italian-Creole-Brooklyn version of an epicurean's fireman's sub. As we finished it, I began to feel a heavy weight in my stomach. I laughingly quizzed Alice about our dinner reservations that were almost eight hours away. I facetiously asked how a ten-inch round, flat loaf of muffuletta bread that had been sliced open and loaded with layers of marinated olive salad, mortadella, salami, mozzarella, ham and provolone, all washed down with two Anchor Steams, could possibly interfere with our dinner appetites? Alice just smiled as she tapped my foot with hers under the table. Before the words, "How about a nap?" had left her mouth, I was signing the bar tab and pushing back from the table. Alice gazed at me with a mischievous smile. Anyone watching might have guessed that we were in love.

But as soon as I pushed open the hotel room door, I knew that something was wrong. Munchie had reappeared from behind the flat-screen TV and was perched on the bed. Tuffy was in her carrier. She wasn't moving. Her motorboat purr was silent. I stooped down to run my hand over her silky head. Her eyes were cracked open and frozen in slits that glazed over with a milky screen. I touched her shoulder; it was hard as stone. I looked back to Alice and she ran toward me. I slipped my hands under Tuffy's side. I could almost lift her like a solid board. Alice turned white and grabbed the phone. I carefully zipped the carrier around my fat-bottomed girl while Alice shakily asked the operator to call a vet.

There was no time for a taxi. We bounded out of the Royal Street door and headed for the French Quarter Animal Clinic two blocks away. With the strap over my shoulder and my right hand gripping the top handle of the carrier I matched Alice stride for stride, who was dashing ahead

158

kicking off her Anne Klein pumps. Somehow, I restrained my urge to shout that a few seconds was not going to make any difference at this point. Alice hit the clinic entrance with tears spilling down her face.

Standing inside the door, dressed in a four-button white lab coat, was a young woman whose face was framed in tight brunette curls. She had been on alert for our arrival and took Alice by the arm, guiding her past three other customers who were gripping their long and short-haired pets close to their chests. I burst in cradling the carrier in both arms.

"Hurry, hurry," Alice exhorted. I followed the two of them through the door marked No Admittance and into a sterile, white examination room. The young veterinarian pointed toward the stainless-steel table in the center of the room. As I lifted the carrier holding Tuffy's stiff body, Alice let out a whimper, and nearly sank to her knees with her hands on the edge of the table. Her pain was stabbing into my stomach like a butcher's blade as the second hand on the wall clock clicked by. Tears burned my squeezed eyes, and I willed the clock to reverse time.

We watched the vet unzip the carrier. As if she were handling nitroglycerine, the vet gently lifted Tuffy's body and reverently placed our little one on the cold, steel table. She extracted a pen case containing a rectal thermometer from her white jacket pocket while pressing her stethoscope against Tuffy's side. After a minute, she read the thermometer and turned to face me and Alice who was now standing upright, holding onto my arm.

"Has your cat been around any toxic substances?' she asked. Alice and I locked eyes.

"What do you mean?" I stammered back. "Isn't Tuffy– Is she dead?"

"No, she's not."

Alice hugged me around my chest as I told the vet we had just arrived today from a road trip, and that Tuffy had

159

been in the hotel room all that time. There was nothing toxic in there.

"Could she have come into contact with anything medicinal?" the vet asked. She could tell from my perplexed look that I was confused. "Such as marijuana?"

"No," we both answered. "Except for this morning," I blurted out. I told the vet about my wrong turn into the city garage, how the pot smell had caught my nose and seeing a fat, still-smoking roach in the coffee tin next to the makeshift office.

"What coffee tin?" Alice said. I told her about what I had seen on the second floor of the garage. Tuffy had been hiding under the chairs in the office when Alice had heard and recovered her. Alice said that she had looked in the coffee tin when she picked up Tuffy, and the tin was empty.

Oh, my God. I had gotten to the garage 20 minutes after Tuffy had escaped. The fat stub of a thick-rolled joint was in the tin when I walked up the ramp to help in the search. If the joint was gone half an hour later when we found Tuffy, then someone or something must have taken it. The vet listened as I reported our adventure.

She held up her hand to stop me, and pointed to the somnambulant feline. "Folks," she said, "your cat is stoned."

"Stoned!" I shouted, grabbing Alice up in my arms, almost delirious with relief that our cat was stoned, not dead. "Will she survive?" I asked as Alice began stroking the still-silent kitty.

"Most likely," the vet answered, and advised us how to proceed. "Be aware that the catatonic condition is temporary, and that stiffness is the muscular reaction dogs and cats have to THC. You need to leave Tuffy in her carrier, unzipped, on the floor, with a large bowl of water nearby. The effects wear off over a ten or twelve--hour period. As the animal regains its mobility, a raging thirst will take over."

Alice and I were at a loss as to how we could thank the vet for being there, but it turned out that a donation to the shelter was sufficient. Before we left, I asked the vet how often she was presented with these kinds of cases.

"At least once a week," she replied. "Especially on weekends when the Quarter is filled with party people drinking and smoking pot." She went on to explain that revelers stroll from one music gig to another, joints burn down to their fingertips, and they drop roaches on the sidewalk or in the street. Feral cats are active in the Quarter after midnight, and during the day the dog walkers are out. Sooner or later a cat or dog will sniff out a roach and munch it down.

"Some feral cats," she continued, "are attracted to the weed like catnip. They are the ones most likely to end up permanently stiff."

Fortunately, our fat-bottomed girl was twice the size of the Quarter's feral cats, and the vet comforted us with the assurance that Tuffy would recover none the worse for her culinary mistake.

A Meal Too Far

Munchie was perched on her haunches just inside the hotel room door, clearly expecting a report on her furry pal's condition. Alice carefully set the carrier down at the foot of the king-sized bed while I filled the Hello Kitty water bowl. Munchie schmoozed up next to Alice, waiting for a signal that it was okay to visit her playmate that was stretched out in the carrier.

Our little terror extended her right socked paw, and ever so softly held it atop Tuffy's drooping whiskers. Sensing the unnatural state of her companion's circumstances, our little Maine Coon, in a totally out-of-character movement, lay down next to the sleeping Tuffy, determined to be there when playtime resumed.

Wasted from the adrenaline rush of our near-death experience, Alice and I collapsed on the bed, content to leave the care of our sleeping stoner in the trusted paws of her faithful friend.

Six hours later and only an hour away before our appointed dinnertime, a clap of thunder that shook and rattled the window glass in our top-floor room awakened us both. Tuffy's status had only changed slightly. She was no longer stiff, and we could see her little chest move up and down. Without a moment to waste, we scrambled into an acceptable state of readiness and headed downstairs.

Stepping from the elevator, we were faced with a crowd dressed in jackets and ties, cocktail dresses, and pantsuits. What at first looked like a queue waiting for some hotel event was soon revealed to be the Royal Street taxi line. The wide front doors of the hotel were flung open to the elements, and throngs of hopeful taxi patrons mingled in the foyer as they awaited their turns. The foyer was filled with the dull roar of sheets of water falling outside, giving proof to the intensity of the storm. Our chance of finding a taxi in time to make our dinner reservation at Gautreau's was in jeopardy.

I guided Alice into the Carousel Bar and spotted Lincoln heading for the service entrance next to the kitchen. He stopped and waited for us to meet him. After a six-hour non-stop bar shift, the erudite professor was eager to get away from the hotel and escape the late-night demands of his job. Alice shoved up close to me as I put my arm on Lincoln's and asked if he could please help us find transportation to our dinner reservation. He laughed good-naturedly and pointed out the foggy bar windows before saying that if we were counting on a taxi, we'd best change our dinner reservations to breakfast. In her most woebegone voice, Alice lamented we would now miss our chance at Gautreau's.

At the sound of the restaurant name, Lincoln's expression changed from amusement to amazement. Without another word, he took Alice by the arm and head-waved me

162

to follow. He waltzed through the kitchen service door with us in his wake. As he parted the kitchen staff for our passage, the men and women in the white chefs' hat tipped their heads and touched two fingers to their hearts in a sign of respect for the most educated bartender in New Orleans. Lincoln turned toward me and said that he didn't know how I had wrangled reservations at Gautreau's but we had better not be late. I shook my head, acknowledging we knew the restaurant was notorious for its severe approach to tardiness. "Better get Uber," was his follow-up.

"We tried Uber, along with everyone else in the hotel," Alice said. I mentioned the Uber wait was an hour even with surge pricing at five times the normal rate.

"Follow me." Lincoln propped open the back door and handed us a golf umbrella as we hurried down the steps and into a private parking zone. Under the umbrella, Lincoln fiddled with his phone and the black Escalade with chrome wheels and dark tinted windows roared to life. Alice jumped into the front, and I slipped into the back seat. Lincoln snapped on the overhead light and slipped his business card into my hand. Alice and I both read *"Your Uber Driver: Professor L.D. Stevens, PhD."*

I clapped our Uber driver on the shoulder and announced, "Professor Emeritus, Carousel bartender and Uber driver rolled into one. Next you'll tell us you also wait tables at Gautreau's."

"No," he said, "but I am the alternate bartender there."

Alice was seldom at a loss for words, but neither of us could express our surprise at this fortunate series of events.

Chapter 9: A Dinner to Remember

"After scolding one's cat, one looks into its face and is seized by the ugly suspicion that it understood every word and has filed it for reference."
Charlotte Gray, character in a novel by Sebastian Faulks

Breaking Bread at Gautreau's

Rain and traffic was turning the ten-minute drive to the Garden District into a half-hour marathon. Lincoln assured us of a safe and timely arrival and suggested that we leave the driving to him. Pelting rain kept the Escalade's wipers swatting at top speed.

By the time Lincoln turned off St. Charles Street, Alice had filled him in on our 'dining with cats' adventure. He had been particularly curious how we obtained reservations at Gautreau's and Alice explained her method of contacting owners and chefs directly when OpenTable or other automatic systems were not available. Alice told Lincoln she was a bit concerned that we were holding reservations for four, and the owner was expecting us with our cats. Lincoln asked why the kitties weren't with us. When Alice told the him why our cats were back at the Monteleone, Lincoln laughed so hard that the car swerved a bit. As we pulled up to the curb on Soniat Street, Lincoln pointed to the front door of the house and said, "Welcome to Gautreau's." He passed us the golf umbrella to shield us from the unyielding downpour, and told us he was bound for a parking spot in back while our path lay up the short walk from the curb.

Lincoln had put our minds at rest about the serious consequences for late arrivals. "These stories are more rumor than fact," he assured us. "Tardiness could cause difficulties, for everyone including the diners, the wait staff and the later arrivals." This was due to the internal logistics, as we would soon find out upon entering.

"Is this it? Do you see a name? Where are we?" Alice asked me as she pulled close beside me under the umbrella. We stood peering through a thin curtain of water at a private residence on a side street in an upscale neighborhood. I pointed at the '1728' brass numbers affixed to one side of the door, affirming that we must be in the right place.

On the left side of the façade, a soft balloon of yellow light billowed through an oversized window framed with paneled drapes. A table, with what appeared to be two people dining, sat inches away from the window. We pushed forward and up the single step into the covered alcove where I closed the umbrella and shook off the water. To our left, a bench attached under a window encrusted with English ivy offered a relaxing spot to enjoy a less humid mid-summer evening. We stood between two brass handrails enclosing the covered alcove that had been placed there for assistance negotiating the single step down to the sidewalk. My palm rose to knock when the door swung open.

"You must be the cat people," were the first words the young lady said after opening the door.

My instinct was to answer "No, we are not cat people. We are hungry humans," but Alice answered first.

"Yes, we are the cat people," she politely responded. Our greeter was wearing kitchen whites with a chef's cap pinned to her hair pulled back tight behind her head. We did not need to see her name (Susan) stitched above the pocket to know one of *James Beard's* and *Top Chef's* most celebrated cooks, was welcoming us to Gautreau's. She motioned us forward, shutting the door standing open to the watery elements outside. From this vantage point, the entire service area was visible.

A dozen tables were set in the open space that was once the floor of an uptown pharmacy. Brentwood chairs were pushed under the white-clothed tables set with crystal water glasses and sterling place settings. Candlesticks in cut-glass holders burned in the center of each table. There was no visible overhead lighting, but the room was sheathed in an incandescence spilling out from the rope lights hidden behind the cornices. In the back arranged like soldiers were bottles of cabernet, pinot and Syrah. They lined the old pharmacy-shelves-turned-bar. Such detail to our surroundings boded well for our dinners.

Alice turned to me and whispered, "Gautreau's is not a restaurant. It's a dinner party. A very, very elegant dinner party."

Swathed in a Parisian elegance, the room was remarkably small. There was no bar, only bar shelves. Once inside the front door, guests are in the restaurant. Looking around at the sparseness of the space framed into the plushness of the setting, I understood what Lincoln had meant about tardiness being a problem of logistics. There was no waiting area. There was no bar. Appointments out of schedule would mean the tardy would be standing around inside, literally looking over the shoulders of fellow diners or standing outside on the sidewalk, waiting for the maître'd to open the door.

Chef pulled out Alice's chair and bent over. I heard her whisper that she had heard about our intoxicated cat. Alice looked at me and we both followed Chef's glance toward the back corner of the pharmacy bar where a tuxedo-clad man (Lincoln) stood with what could only be a Kentucky Mule copper mug on top of his tray. He had told Chef about our 'dining and driving with cats' as well as the day's mishap with Tuffy and the controlled substance.

Chef told us she had made the trip from Wilkes-Barre to New Orleans in a Fiat 500 with three cats. After fourteen hours with three felines scratching and pawing for attention, she wished for some pot. We laughed and asked whether she meant for the three cats or herself?

"What do you think?" she answered, laughing, and told us that cat lovers are always welcome at Gautreau's.

"Tonight," Chef Susan said, "we are offering a chance to experience our menu by serving you a few cat-sized samples." Wondering what 'cat-sized samples' might actually be, we waved at Lincoln as he crossed the room bearing a surprise for Alice.

"One Kentucky Mule." He beamed as he set down the copper mug in front of her. "Prepared exactly how you like it."

My eyebrows shot up and I could not restrain myself from saying, "No Way."

"Way," he said, clasping his hands as he spoke the three sacred words: "Pappy Van Winkle."

Alice now took up the chant, "No Way!"

"Way," he repeated, as Alice raised the copper cup to her lips and sipped a taste of the spicy nectar.

Kentucky Mule Recipe
Highball glass filled with ice
2oz. Pappy Van Winkle (Makers Mark substitute)
Fill with Ginger Beer – Powell & Mahoney preferred
May add 1 tbsp. simple syrup or 1 tsp. powdered sugar to soften the ginger
1 Kentucky splash of Rose's Lime Juice (may substitute juice of real lemon)
Garnish with lime slice.

"Please make mine a Vieux Carre with Bulleit Rye," I chimed, in wanting to get in on this celebration as soon as possible.

Lincoln nodded and turned back to the bar as our tuxedo-clad server approached us with hand-lettered menus. Everything was marked seasonal, and the printed annotation informed us that every food item used in the kitchen had been locally sourced.

My eyes widened as they scanned the night's choices. "Greens!" I whispered, "and squash too."

Alice shushed me with her finger. Other guests were listening. Inadvertent eavesdropping is an unintended consequence of maximizing serving space in such a restricted area. Of course, we soon discovered that when the tables were filled with guests, no one could overhear anyone's conversation. With as many as two dozen dinner patrons seated in such compressed environs, the competition for air space was noticeable. On the bright side, the myriad conversations fractured into wall-to-wall jangling consonants, which effectively blocked any chance of eavesdropping.

By the time Lincoln returned with my Vieux Carre, half the tables were filled, and he had taken up a full-time stance at the end of the pharmacy shelves where a Pappy Van Winkle 20-Year Reserve was perched on the top rack. I perused the menu and Alice pointed to various choices.

"Greens," I announced again, pointing at the *Red Snapper with Swiss Chard, Sweet Potatoes and Mustard Vinaigrette.* "More greens," I continued, underlining the braised kale served with the *Seared Pork Chop with Natural Jus.*

"Mustard greens," I whispered tapping on the *Beet and Ricotta Gnocchi.* "Chef serves pasta over my favorite plant: mustard greens."

Slightly annoyed at my exuberance over Gautreau's fascination with leafy greens, Alice stuck her menu in front of me and she whispered with sarcasm, "Don't miss the spinach. It's just the way you like it."

Alice was right. Our menu also listed a *Sautéed Cobia with Champagne Beurre Blanc* served over a deep-green layer of wilted spinach.

Alice enjoyed teasing me about my fetish for firm-fleshed white fish sautéed in butter and olive oil and served smoking hot over wilted or sautéed leafy greens. She knew I could eat this combination every night, and had missed it during the three years we lived in Mexico. In particular, it was the fish that I missed. My taste for greens was easy to satisfy in Mexico. Every backyard garden in San Miguel grew collard greens, turnip greens, mustard greens, chard and kale and the greens always found their way onto my plate almost nightly, even if they were covered by burritos, enchiladas, tacos or fajitas.

Alice had never developed the same taste for leafy greens. Instead she was content to obtain her minimum daily requirement of cruciferous vegetables with asparagus, broccoli and Brussels sprouts. My obsessiveness over building a meal around these plant foods was the source of our first lover's quarrel.

Alice Has a Nose for Greens

Shortly after moving in with me, Alice persuaded me to cut back on our restaurant dining and spend more evenings at home together. This required me to memorize the phone number for Two Brother's Pizza, Geronimo Subs, Bernie's Wings and Ching's Chinese. For several weeks, the closest I came to a leafy green vegetable was the bok choy in Ching's Lo Mein Noodles. At the time, I didn't cook and Alice had no intention of taking on that responsibility after a rough day at work. She had employed her superior mental skills to persuade me that putting food on the table was my responsibility. A folded piece of paper in her left hand had the names of five food delivery and takeout spots she had settled on. She curled my fingers around the paper and told me that I needed to find their phone numbers and map their locations.

An hour later, my mission had been accomplished. Alice had given me every reason to believe that my success in this endeavor would lead to a special reward. I tacked the list onto the refrigerator door and headed to the bedroom to claim my prize, only to discover Alice asleep under the covers with Evie Mae stretched out on the small of her back. LeRoy was perched on the backs of her legs. Eying my entry, LeRoy's top lip twitched in a 'Don't Even Think of It' warning as I approached the bed. Just standing over the bed watching my Rockette girl's sleeping form rise and fall blissfully made my heart swell.

My duty as chief food provider continued without incident for three weeks until Alice was enjoying every pizza, wing and fried rice dish while I was miserable at the nutritional insolvency of our dinners. I had already taken to buying frozen bags of Birdseye spinach and collard greens and heating them up to accompany the diet Alice was determined to follow.

One night, she arrived home to find a thick pan-fried pork chop on her plate. It was surrounded by a layer of braised lemon-garlic kale and snow peas mixed with quinoa. I had worked hard to prepare that meal, but Alice lifted the plate and said, "Where are the wings?"

At that point, I proceeded to lecture her on the merits of a balanced diet and the dangers of trans-fat, high-carb foods. I relayed how much I enjoyed green leafy vegetables and how much I missed my mother's cooking.

That was it. Hiroshima, Nagasaki – nothing compared to Alice when she was really angry. I could see that my loving words about my mother's cooking had hurt her more than sticks and stones.

Alice rose to her full height, which was still about a foot shorter than mine, and said she would be happy to rent me a Jolly Green Giant suit so she could continue to be reminded of my love for green vegetables. As I began to object, she held up her hand and said, "I think you also should carve out some quality time to spend alone with your memories of your mother's cooking." After a pause, she added, "Maybe we should have waited longer to move in together."

170

I took the only road available for a man whose back was against the wall and knows that his heart and soul are in jeopardy: I surrendered. I fell to my knees, bowed my head and confessed that I was wrong. She was right; I had no right to lecture her. I asked her to forgive my words and deeds, and give me a chance to show that I loved her more than life itself.

Her countenance changed. The flush fell from her cheeks. Her shoulders –so tense the previous second – now sagged. She asked why I hadn't made any suggestions before tonight's surprise, that her list of food sources was certainly negotiable, and that, frankly, she was getting rather bored with the menus.

When I heard her next words, I knew we could recover. "Am I still your Rockette girl?" My smile came from inside my heart. I think she felt it spill across the floor and flow to her.

Our happy epilogue was a mature discussion about the importance of healthy eating and how the two of us could find it together at the dinner table. We resolved that I would keep food on the table per her wants and preferences. In exchange, she would accept that my dinners would include fresh, green vegetables.

Tapping my menu, Alice brought me back to our table at Gautreau's where our server had looked over twice to see if we were ready to order.

Even though I wasn't ready, I signaled to the server. "This is a difficult decision," I whispered. Three of my favorite starters were on the appetizer list.

"*Foie Gras!*" suggested Alice. It was one of her favorites, too.

"You might enjoy the *Mascarpone Agnolotti*," suggested the server.

"Oh yes," I responded. "I'm sure my wife would love to try your *English Pea and Mascarpone Agnolotti with Sugar Snap Peas, Lemon and Mint*." Peas were to Alice as

171

oil is to water. My Rockette girl would not even eat fried rice until she had deftly flicked out every tiny green pea. I quickly corrected my order as Alice growled under her breath. "On second thought," I said, "maybe we should try the *Spicy Sautéed Shrimp with Thai Basil-Lime Vinaigrette, Roasted Avocado, Melon and Pineapple Salsa,*"

Alice smiled and said, "As good as the shrimp sounds, I'd rather have the *Duck Confit* – but please hold the spinach."

I laughed as our server scribbled her request. I went on to say, "But the *Confit in Sherry-Mustard Vinaigrette with Asian Pears, Apples, and Cantal Cheese* would look lonely without the spinach." I could not hide a sly grin as I pushed more green things at my Rockette.

Alice feigned a snarl at my teasing and said, "No. No spinach".

I settled on the *Foie Gras Torchon* even though the *Crispy Sweetbreads with the Pimenton Gastrique* attracted my attention. I suggested to our server he might want to turn in our appetizers while we debated our entrée choice.

As our waiter headed toward the kitchen, Alice rapped my knuckle and said, "Why couldn't you order now? We both know you're going to order the fish. You always order the fish."

The Secret of Life

Alice was probably right, but the question was which fish and with which sauce? Looking at the menu items, it was evident Chef had distinguished herself through her innovative use of sauces. She had cleverly paired many menu selections with a distinctive garnish or sauce to both enhance the main dish and integrate the flavors of all the elements. I noticed this creative combination with the appetizers and asked Alice to confirm my observation. The *Thai Basil-Lime Vinaigrette* was paired with the *Pineapple Salsa* for the *Spicy*

Sautéed Shrimp appetizer, and the *Poblano Creama* was a perfect foil for the *Sea Scallops*. So was the *Sherry-Mustard Vinaigrette* that Alice would soon be enjoying with her *Duck Confit* and the *Red-Onion Bourbon Marmalade* that would electrify my *Foie Gras with Poached Peach*.

"It's not just the appetizers," Alice said as she pointed to the pork chop. "Could there be a more estimable sauce for a *Seared Pork Chop than its Natural Jus?*"

"And what about the *Sautéed Cobia in a Champagne Beurre Blanc Sauce?*"

Alice quickly jumped to the *Beet and Ricotta Gnocchi* and asked the obvious. "Could there be a more perfect pairing for this dish than a *Pecan-Sage Brown Butter Sauce?*"

"No," came a voice from behind us. We turned to see Chef smiling at us. Alice and I instinctively cringed.

" The *Pecan-Sage Brown Butter* is one of my favorite sauces for any type of pasta," she said. Then she pointed to the *Angus Filet* that was served with a *Bordelaise Sauce* and the *Seared Duck Breast* paired with a *Fig Demi-Glace*.

Chef agreed we had found the magic made only at Gautreau's. The sauce pairings explained why Gautreau's was the hottest ticket in town with a fan base spread around the world.

Chef kneeled down between us and, at eye level, asked if we had read Fanny Flagg's hilarious book, *Fried Green Tomatoes*. We nodded, "yes", and joined Chef in repeating Fanny Flagg's world-famous quote: *"The secret of life? The secret's in the sauce!"*

The only way our dinner at Gautreau's could have been any more enjoyable would have been if Tuffy and Munchie had been able to join us. No doubt, our lobster lover would have enjoyed a taste of the *Sautéed Cobia,* while Tuffy would have licked away at the gnocchi.

To our surprise, what arrived at our table for starters were two serving plates separated into six tiny, bite-sized

173

portions from the appetizer list. Alice pierced the *Spicy Shrimp* as I licked my fork smeared with the *Thai Basil-Lime Vinaigrette and Pineapple Salsa*. The citrus and salsa had my toes dancing in my shoes, and Alice added with unintended sarcasm, "The *Sautéed Spicy Shrimp* wasn't so bad, either." My newfound love for *Seared Scallops in a Poblano Creama Sauce* is 100% due to my one taste at Gautreau's.

Alice left one sweetbread bite, drizzled with paprika, for me. With this tiny morsel, Gautreau's has introduced the planet's second food item that competes with 'Frito-Lay Que No Puedes Comer Solo Una,' the Mexican version of 'Bet you can't eat just one.'

We saved our miniature portions of *Foie Gras Torchon* and *Duck Confit* for last. Chef had presented us with a deliciously plump duck thigh for the confit. Alice took one bite and swiftly moved the portion out of my reach. After graciously offering her a bite of my tiny torchon, she took mercy on me and let me taste the confit. Alice watched as I felt my mouth explode with the flavors absorbed into the duck fat on a thigh with a skin so perfectly toasted that it bubbled. She winked and said, "Argent."

"Yes," I said, remembering back over 30 years ago when on a cold, wintry night in Paris we had maxed out our Visa card on a cash advance to pay for our one haute cuisine meal at La Tour D'Argent. Neither of us had ever tasted anything as divine as the *Silver Tower's Duck Confit*. At least that was true until we arrived at Gautreau's.

With our bite-sized appetizers settling within, we sat back as our server arrived with my main dish. I had astonished Alice by ordering the *Angus Beef Filet* rather than a seafood dish. I held up one finger and said those five dangerous words: "I know what I'm doing."

This time, I was right; I did know what I was doing. After the first bite of this perfectly prepared piece of meat, I sliced off a strip drenched in bordelaise sauce and deftly placed it in Alice's open mouth. Her eyes said it all. This was

174

the best filet either of us had ever tasted. I had ordered this delicacy on impulse, believing that Chef would not have this item on the menu purely to please her meat-loving patrons. She was a genius at sauces, and the only reason she would plate a filet would be if she could pair it with a sauce that would bring out a taste that would rival any steakhouse from Manhattan to Houston.

Admitting a dining preference for seafood dishes, my recommendation on this entrée might not carry much weight. Alice, on the other hand, is incredibly discerning, one might even say picky, when it comes to red meat. She does not hesitate to push away a $52 filet at Trulucks or a $45 ribeye from Ruth's Chris if it doesn't melt on her tongue. I never argue the point. I always pay up and take the remains home. Fortunately for me, Alice's main order arrived just as she was about to reach across the table to pull more of my filet onto her plate. I think she liked it.

Alice Discovers Grandma's Chicken

Immediately after our appetizer bite of Duck Confit, Alice had called our server and changed her order from the Gnocchi to the Roasted Chicken with Rosemary Jus. As the server set the half portion of golden-tinted and crinkle-skinned bird on the table, Alice and I crossed our fingers as she made the wish she had made at least 50 times in our dining lives.

"Please be Grandma's Sunday poulet roti." Alice had made this wish in every restaurant in D.C., New York, and Chicago that had roasted chicken on the menu since returning from our busman's holiday in Paris where we had spent our last dime splurging at La Tour D'Argent. We had walked out of the Silver Tower with only enough cash for a second-class fare on the train to Charles De Gaulle Airport, and less than 60 francs ($8) per day to live on for seven days until flying home. If we were going to survive another seven nights in the

City of Lights on a Parisian college student's allowance, we needed a plan. The next evening with less than $10 to spend for dinner we headed out with Alice's plan.

All I had to do was figure out how to get us across town from the Sacre Coeur district to the Sorbonne University district. We decided to walk even though the Metro ran by St. Michael's station a few blocks from the University. Walking would save us a few francs and give us a better chance of finding the Parisian version of affordable dining. As we walked, we didn't see any signboards with items that cost less than 50 francs per course. We couldn't afford to spend our daily allotment of 60 francs all on one course.

We arrived at the University in the late afternoon when classes were ending. Students of every nationality, weighed down with suitcase-sized backpacks of books and belongings, trudged toward us down the sidewalk. Alice focused on two young men wearing heavy pea jackets with frayed sleeves and missing buttons on the cuffs. Their shoes were lace ups and as sharp as any seen on a banker or diplomat. That was the clue. We followed them to the edge of the Latin Quarter where they headed toward the open-air Buci Market. It was lined with outdoor stalls that displayed produce, cheese and plucked chickens hanging from thin metal hooks.

The students stopped at a narrow doorway with only the word 'Procope' above it. A chalkboard was nailed to the wall. We followed the young men up a steep stairwell into a second-floor loft with a high A-frame ceiling and picnic-style tables and benches neatly arranged within the space. They slid onto opposite benches. Alice pulled us to sit down beside them. Alice was almost jammed against the student who took no notice of our presence. He continued his conversation with his classmate until a wide, middle-aged man sheathed in a white apron came over and asked the four of us for our order. Alice's new seatmate pointed to the chalkboard, as did his classmate. Alice looked at the waiter, held up two fingers and said, "Deux." Two more male students sat down across from us, making six at our table. They also pointed to the card that read, '*Poulet Roti Frites et Vin 30f.*'

The waiter returned carrying a basket with loose knives, forks, spoons and glasses stacked inside. He rolled a handful of utensils onto the table and slapped down six, large water glasses. My eyes were getting bigger, wondering what was happening, but Alice squeezed my hand asked me how I had enjoyed the Monet lilies on the basement walls of the Jeu de Paume.

The students interrupted their animated conversations. "American?" two of them asked.

We nodded. One student asked, in English, how we had found this place. Alice's seatmate answered that we had not found it but had followed them.

Alice asked him how he knew we had followed them. He said that we were not the first broke American tourists smart enough to follow Sorbonne students to find quality French food at ridiculously low prices. He asked why Alice chose to follow him rather than some other student. Alice said it was obvious that he and his friend knew how to make choices in spending their allowance. She took the collar of his pea coat in one hand. "Your mother will repair your coat on your next visit home, non?" She also admitted that the quality of their shoes indicated that they were accustomed to quality dining. Everyone at the table laughingly enjoyed Alice's reasoning.

The waiter sat down a magnum of red wine labeled *Bonne.* Alice filled each of the six glasses, and together we toasted something unrecognizable in French. Before we could get a second quaff, the waiter returned with six plates that each held one quarter of a roasted chicken topped off with hand-cut, twice-fried, slender potatoes and a heaping spoonful of neatly sliced and buttered yellow carrots. Alice and I exchanged our thighs and legs for our neighbors' wings and breasts.

Alice took one forkful of the crispy, succulent rosemary-herbed chicken and her taste for meat versus poultry changed for good. Alice loved red meat, but after her first 'poulet roti,' she would never go back. Like Alice, I was totally amazed by the taste of the birds with sticky, salty skin and falling-off-the-bone-tender meat. The moist, juicy texture, and rich herbed flavor was, in the words of Julia Child, "Simply delicious." The young men told us that this particular dish was known as *Grandma's Sunday Chicken,* and was one of the city's most iconic meals. It was the only place that Voltaire would take his Sunday dinners. He had sat at these same tables in the 18th century to dine on *Grandma's Sunday Chicken.*

Our seatmates talked over each other explaining the reason for the scrumptious fowl. France takes its chicken very seriously, and Sunday birds are pasture raised. In the Buci Market, the butchers and homemakers accept only two brands of chicken: chicken 'crapaudine' (a most unfortunate name for an excellent bird) and *'poulet de Bresse.'* Twice as expensive due to its size, the Bresse didn't fit the budget of the Procope clientele. The crapaudine or spatchcocked birds are every bit as tasty as their expensive cousins and the only bird roasted at Cafe Procope. In addition to their pasture-raised guarantee, the birds had been marinated for several days in a variety of ingredients, ranging from citrus and ginger to honey and sesame. Each is roasted until the skin is extra crispy. The only drawback to our discovery and ensuing enchantment with the flavor of Cafe Procope's *Crapaudine Poulet* is that the delicious taste is as rare in American restaurants as crapaudine hens' teeth.

As Alice took her second forkful of Gautreau's rosemary-herbed poulet roti, a huge smile spread across her face. My Rockette girl was happy and so was I. Before the roasted chicken disappeared completely, I suggested that Alice slice off a few pieces for our furry friends back at the Monteleone.

At this point in our meal, there was nothing left to do except order the *Caramelized Banana Split with Vanilla Ice Cream with Warm Banana Bread, Butterscotch, Chocolate Sauce and Toasted Walnuts.* Alice requested a Baileys on the rocks while I signaled to Lincoln to bring over a shot of Pappy's, neat.

As our server appeared with the damage report disguised as our bill, Alice asked if "l'addition" was more than our entire bill at Procope's.

"Slightly more," I said, "But cheap at twice the price!" *(Today's Procope advertises to a well-heeled clientele that can afford to dine in the luxurious surroundings of not only the oldest café in Paris but one of its highest rated brasseries. The rustic charm has been replaced with white table cloths)*

Return to Tuffy

By the time our taxi delivered us back to the Monteleone, the late-night crowd was jammed into the Carousel Bar. Alice was as eager to get upstairs and see about our cannabis kitty and I was lightheaded from the last Pappy's.

We were greeted by Munchie who immediately rolled onto her back, coyly inviting us to rub her tummy (which would only end in a sharp stinging swipe from her claws). Snoozing loudly in the center of the bed was the object of our attention; Tuffy did not move when we entered. Alice sat down by the medicinally restrained kitty and gently fluffed her thick coat. The motorboat purr soon filled the air. Her bowl of water was nearly empty and, as the vet had predicted, our fat-bottomed girl was no worse for her adventure.

Our next day's plans included a trip to the Chalmette Battlefield. If Tuffy appeared to be back to normal by morning, we would take our little pals along for the paddlewheel boat ride down to Jean Lafitte National Park and tour the famous Andrew Jackson victory site. This was a tour for which Alice had expressed an unusual amount of interest. The only thing that would stop us would be the New

Orleans summer weather that could ruin the event. Although rain was not a big deterrent for Alice or me, the kitties had a definite problem with it.

Before turning off the lights for the night, Alice said she would like to have beignets for breakfast. That meant an early morning walk to Café du Monde near Jackson Square where the beignets were from heaven and the coffee was from that other place. When the coffee is so bad that you remember it after six years, you know it's really bad. Actually, it wasn't that it was bad coffee; it was chicory masquerading as coffee. Fortunately, the Café du Monde also made a decent cappuccino. With that thought in my head, we closed our eyes.

Chapter 10: Battlefields and Pirates

"Cats seem to go on the principle that it never does any harm to ask for what you want." Joseph Wood Crutch

Breakfast at Tiffany's — Sorta

No one except Alice ever accused me of looking like George Peppard, and Alice is too short and blonde to be confused with Audrey Hepburn. Nevertheless, just like Holly Golightly, we both like standing up, eating pastries and drinking coffee. And of course, there is 'that cat.' Most people remember the opening scene of *Breakfast at Tiffany's* in which Audrey Hepburn stands in front of Tiffany's holding a coffee cup and pastry when Peppard walks by, but not many fans remember the cat. Alice had been in grade school when she and her older sister went to see *Breakfast at Tiffany's*. Alice couldn't forget her negative adrenaline rush when George and Audrey pushed the poor kitty out of the taxi and into the rain. The kitty was a bedraggled waif that was only saved from the terrors of Manhattan when the two star-crossed lovers simultaneously leapt from their taxi into the downpour to rescue the helpless cat.

Cafe du Monde may not look exactly like Tiffany's in New York, but when you stand on Decatur Street at 8:00 a.m. with a cat carrier slung over one shoulder as you stare at the white-faced mimes and gypsy palm readers across the street while squeezing a scalding cappuccino in one hand and slapping powdered sugar from a chewy beignet off your nose and clothes, the only thing missing is a yellow cab dropping off George Peppard and Audrey Hepburn clutching her coffee and pastry.

We spotted a couple about to vacate a bench near the Cafe's 'to go' window. I pushed through the line and patted down a comfortable spot for Alice scurrying over with Munchie to join me. Alice lifted the carrier onto her lap when she remembered having stuffed the Café du Monde bag holding our third beignet into the carrier that held Munchie. As the carrier tilted on her lap, the powdery beignet tumbled out of the bag and bumped into the kitties twitching whiskers. Munchie was startled by the sudden appearance of the snowy pastry and began swatting at it. Each swat raised a dust cloud of powdered sugar. We could only giggle as our kitty turned into a furry snowball. Alice sent me to fetch a bottle of water and paper towels. When I returned, Alice was holding Munchie on her lap wrapped in a towel. Beside her sat a young man wearing a cobalt blue *New Orleans Docent Walking Tour* shirt.

His name was Joseph, and he was a rising sophomore at Tulane spending his summer as a volunteer docent for the Chalmette Battlefield. He lived on gratuities he collected at the end of each tour. Meeting a man, not yet twenty, who possessed enough knowledge of historical facts to be a Chalmette Battlefield docent was a bit surprising, and I wondered how he had come in possession of his expertise. When Alice told him that we planned to visit the Chalmette Battlefield that afternoon, Joseph started fidgeting with eagerness to tell us what he knew of the place, but the noise of tourists, panhandlers and amateur musicians along Decatur Street made it difficult for the three of us to have a conversation. The young tour guide suggested we move our impromptu meeting across the street to the La Divina cafe next to the St. Louis Cathedral. We agreed, and in exchange for a small gratuity paid in coffee and cinnamon buns, Alice and I would get a preview of our afternoon site visit to the Chalmette Battlefield.

Once settled into the cushioned metal chairs at the La Divina, our docent asked if he could hold one of our kitties. Alice volunteered Tuffy, knowing how much our fat-bottomed girl loved exploring new laps. As the young man pulled the fat, black kitty onto his lap, Alice and I saw his eyes misting. Holding back the tears, our cat-loving friend told us he had left his own special friend, a gray tabby, back at home when he accepted a scholarship offer at Tulane. Joseph's kitty had been his constant companion throughout his life. Two weeks ago, after Joseph had completed a day of leading tours at the battlefield, he found a message from his mother at the boarding house where he lived. When he returned the call, he learned that his feline friend had died of what his mother could only describe as a 'broken heart.'

Left alone for the first time in fifteen years, his pet could not adapt to an empty room or house without Joseph. She had spent her nights since he had left padding back and forth, looking for her human friend. Exhausted from the unceasing search, the tabby had climbed on to the pillow where she and Joseph had slept every night for the past fifteen years. Curled on the pillow with her striped tail over her eyes, she faded away with Joseph's sweet smell from the pillow lingering in her nose.

Realizing how close my Alice was to tears over this story, I changed the subject back to the battlefield by asking Joseph a few questions about the famous battle that had occurred there. He wiped at his tears and ran his fingers through his reddish hair until he was composed and ready to talk.

Johnny Horton Sings a Tune

Alice volunteered that until this trip, the only thing she remembered from her college history class about the War of 1812 was that the British burned down the White House. I admitted that most of my knowledge came from Johnny Horton. My mention of the name elicited a muffled laugh from Joseph and a puzzled look from Alice. After he stopped laughing, Joseph cocked an eyebrow and said he was convinced that the Boomer generation derived most of its historical information from music. Every Boomer he had guided that summer could sing half of a stanza of Johnny

Horton's number one hit on *Billboard, The Battle of New Orleans.*

> *"In 1814 we took a little trip*
> *Along with Colonel Jackson down the mighty*
> *Mississip'*
> *We took a little bacon and we took a little beans*
> *And we caught the bloody British in the town of New*
> *Orleans"*

"Everyone over the age of 40, chimed in for the chorus," Joseph continued.

> *"Yeah, they ran through the briers*
> *and they ran through the brambles*
> *And they ran through the bushes*
> *where a rabbit couldn't go*
> *They ran so fast*
> *that the hounds couldn't catch 'em*
> *On down the Mississippi*
> *to the Gulf of Mexico"*

I surprised Joseph and Alice when I correctly sang out the next stanzas of Horton's song. I explained how I had memorized the unabridged lyrics as an extra credit report for my 10th grade history test:

> *"Well, I seed Mars Jackson come a walkin' down the*
> *street*
> *Talkin' to a pirate by the name of Jean Lafitte*
> *He gave Jean a drink that he brung from Tennessee*
> *And the pirate said he'd help drive the British in the sea"*

> *"Well the French told Andrew 'You had better run,*
> *For Packingham's a comin' with a bullet in his gun*
> *Ole Hickory said he didn't give a damn,*

184

He's a-gonna whup the britches off of Colonel Packingham"

Joseph pointed out that the last two stanzas were critical for understanding how the War was actually won, even though the song had taken liberties with the spelling of Colonel Pakenham's name as 'Packingham.'

"But more to the point," he complained, "most people, certainly none of my visitors this year had a clue what they were singing about."

Joseph went on to explain that most of his sightseers didn't know who was running through the bushes, and only one person had any idea who Colonel Packenham was.

"Even worse," he continued, "no one seemed to understand how important the War of 1812 was for preserving the United States as a sovereign country. Most school kids leave high school thinking that the surrender of British General Cornwallis to George Washington at Yorktown brought an end of British aggression."

Joseph was right about that. This was the first I had heard that the British were notorious "treaty cheaters" who intended to break the U.S.-England treaty at the first opportunity. Our docent was clearly passionate about the subject and upset that all good, red-blooded American citizens didn't feel as strongly about it as he did.

At this juncture, it wasn't possible to hide my sheepish grin. I readily admitted to being almost ignorant of what the whole war had been about and had no inkling that it was important to America staying a free and independent country. In fact, the only thing I knew for certain about the War of 1812 was that, according to Johnny Horton, it was fought in 1814 and that Andrew Jackson's nickname had been Ole Hickory. As far as the tune's reference to Colonel 'Packing-ham,' it seemed like one of those clever names Andrew Jackson might have called his horse.

185

Joseph made a determined effort to educate me. He started by telling us that the Johnny Horton tune had done more harm than good. His tune had left everyone believing the famous battle on Chalmette was in 1814.

"The actual battle date that sent the British running through the bushes 'where a rabbit couldn't go' happened on a foggy, wintry day in January of 1815."

I innocently asked our docent to at least confirm that Andrew Jackson had won the Battle of New Orleans. His answer shocked us both.

"Andrew Jackson received the credit for the win because he was the Commanding General, but the battle was won by Jean Lafitte."

"The pirate?" said Alice. She had paged through the hotel's bedside copy of *The Visitor's Guide to New Orleans*, which had a short story about the National Park named for Jean Lafitte. When Alice told me that our site visit to the Chalmette Battlefield was part of the Jean Laffite National Park, I was really confused. I had thought the pirates had been in league with the British.

Alice asked Joseph how he knew so much about this subject as she reached over to stroke Tuffy, still sprawled on Joseph's lap. He pulled a manuscript out of his backpack and placed it on the table. It was titled *Jean Laffite and the Battle of New Orleans* by Joseph L. Poincette. The L. stood for Lafitte. Our docent guide, with whom we shared cinnamon buns and coffee, was a direct descendant of the pirate.

As a child, Joseph had been fascinated by his genealogy that connected him to the famous pirate who, he claimed, won the Battle of New Orleans. His efforts to research and compile the factual history of his great, great grandfather culminated in the manuscript he laid before us. Under the title was the logo and mark of the publishing proof by the November Quarterly of the *Southern Historical Journal*. Joseph, a Louisiana teenager, had successfully submitted a research paper to one of America's most prestigious history journals that had reviewed, accepted and published it. After it was published, he submitted the *Pirate Lafitte* article as his entrance essay on his Tulane University application. Impressed that a seventeen-year old applicant had published in a journal that was beyond the reach of many tenured faculty, the University had offered Joseph L. Poincette a full academic scholarship. As Joseph completed his story, Alice suggested we order another round of cappuccinos and let our docent tell us everything we should have learned in school about the Battle of New Orleans.

My first question was about the importance of the war. Joseph had already said that the War of 1812 was important to preserving the sovereignty of the United States. British pride had not allowed them to accept loss of the colonies as a permanent arrangement, and the War of 1812 was the opportunity that London aristocrats had been waiting for to reunite the colony states with their mother country.

Many of the colonists who had penned their names to the Constitution of 1789 were still alive when President James Madison signed a declaration of war. The British had embargoed U.S. goods, provided provisions to native American tribes and committed other aggressive acts with the intent of starting a war. This was the first I heard about Britain intentionally stirring up a hornet's nest in the new United States in order to start a war they expected to win.

"If Britain had won, they would have taken over the administration of the U.S. through military might," continued our young docent.

Take us over? I thought to myself. Hadn't George Washington defeated the British and won our independence at Yorktown? I was suddenly interested in what had been at the core of this peculiar state of affairs.

Jefferson Buys a Bridge

Joseph took note of my puzzled expression and said, "The whole affair was related to the Louisiana Purchase." At the mention of this most famous American deal, Alice and I gave Joseph our undivided attention.

Joseph sat up straight and held up one finger assuring our attention. He began to explain that when Thomas Jefferson was elected President, he wanted to make a bold statement of his presidency by buying half of what is now the U.S. but was then 'French Territory.'

"But," went on our docent, "it wasn't actually the French Government that sold Jefferson the Territory."

Alice and I both turned to face one another with an obvious question on our lips. "If the French didn't sell Jefferson the Louisiana Purchase who did?"

Joseph answered, "It was a man who claimed to own half of the land in the future U.S., and said he had the authority to sell it. The man was a little guy from Corsica with a big ego who went by the name of Napoleon Bonaparte."

"Wasn't he in charge back then?" interrupted Alice before I could get the same words out. "Wasn't he authorized to make the deal?"

"Only in his own mind," answered Joseph. "Napoleon was a thorn in the side of the British, constantly stirring up crowds and starting wars with a lot of people dying as a result. When he finally declared himself Emperor of France, the British would not recognize him as a legitimate leader."

"Whoa!" I jumped in to interrupt Joseph. "Did that mean Thomas Jefferson was like the rube in Iowa who thought he could buy the Brooklyn Bridge?"

"Yes, precisely," agreed Joseph staring to chuckle at my crude comparison. "In fact", went on Joseph, "the British never accepted the Louisiana Purchase as a bona fide

188

transaction. As far as they were concerned the land still belonged to Spain and there was never a legitimate French claim. Furthermore," continued Joseph, "the British insisted, and British law confirmed, that Bonaparte was a usurper, a petty tyrant who did not have the authority of the French people to make such a deal. The British held that the territory was still a Spanish property."

Alice scrunched forward and asked "what difference did it make for Britain to say the Louisiana Territory was actually a Spanish property rather than French?"

"It made a difference," responded Joseph, "because by the time of the Battle of New Orleans Britain and France were also engaged in a titanic struggle on sea and land that ended at Waterloo. It was a foregone conclusion that if the British defeated Napoleon, the Louisiana Territory would be returned to Spain as compensation for their assistance."

"But the British did defeat Napoleon – at Waterloo," jumped in Alice.

"Yes," answered Joseph, "but that was 1815 – a year after the Battle of New Orleans."

"I get it," I chimed in now realizing how important the New Orleans battle was for the US future.

"It was of paramount importance that the US prevailed in the War of 1812," agreed Joseph. "And, winning the war came down to one crucial battle: The Battle of New Orleans. Not only were the British going to turn back the clock on the Louisiana Purchase and return the property rights to Spain but as soon as the British took over New Orleans they intended to merge the New Orleans British Army with the British Army coming down the Mississippi from Canada to hold the U.S. prisoner within our own borders."

As Joseph explained this, it became clearer why the Battle of New Orleans was such an important victory. It put our destiny in our own hands once and for all. If we had lost at Chalmette Battlefield, life would have been quite different.

Rather than enjoying our visit dining on beignets and cappuccino, Alice and I could have been sipping tea and eating spotted dick. Listening to Joseph explain this important moment, I could almost visualize the images Joseph described.

Alice and I were on our third cappuccino by the time Joseph got to the part about the role his great, great grandfather, Jean Lafitte, had played in sending the British 'running through the bush.' By now it was time for Joseph to head out to Chalmette for his guide duties. We thanked him for sharing all his knowledge and promised to be there for either his 2:00 p.m. or 3:00 p.m. tour, along with Munchie and Tuffy. As we parted, Joseph recommended the Fleur de Lis on Royal Street for lunch. They had an open-air patio with a covered roof, and it was an historic venue. Joseph left us saying that his ancestor, Jean Lafitte, had fought three duels at the Fleur de Lis under the giant willow tree.

When we entered the side door of the Fleur de Lis, we spotted a willow tree, as thick and round as two oil drums, growing in the center patio straight up through the lattice covered roof. A waiter escorted us to a table for four already set with dinnerware in a prime location under the willow. Fans in the covered patio blew a refreshing breeze over us as I studied the lengthy menu. Alice let the kitties squirm out of their carriers and onto her lap, but kept them well-harnessed by their kitty leashes.

Wrangling both at once was more art than science. When Munchie and Tuffy were on my lap, they acted like Scottie dog magnets that alternatively attracted and repelled each other. One or the other kitty would jump from my lap without warning. With Alice, they sit side by side, ignoring each other but seemingly content to lie still as Alice slowly strokes them into a combined purr. Our waiter, seeing the two felines stretched out on Alice's lap, almost tip-toed over to our table to deliver our lunch orders.

Alice could tell from the grimace on my face that my lunch disagreed with me. Lump crabmeat blended with a mayonnaise and infused with a lemony taste looked and sounded better than it actually was. Arriving at our table so quickly, literally minutes after I ordered it, should have been a clue. Such a popular midday course was likely to have been prepared early in the day. After my first bite, I knew that the salad had either not been properly cooled or had sat in the hot and humid surroundings of the enclosed patio for several hours. A second bite confirmed the first and soon had me so nauseous that it was impossible to disguise my condition from Alice. Realizing my distress, but not yet certain of the cause, we hurriedly paid and left the patio to head back to our hotel.

Minutes later, our little terror found me on my knees with my head bent over the toilet bowl. Why the sound of my violent retching so intrigued the little Maine Coon I don't know, but she stood on her hind legs with both front paws resting on my arm that was curled over the top of the toilet bowl. Glad for the company, I was careful to keep my arm in place so as not to disturb her obvious curiosity.

Alice found the scene more than just disturbing. She plucked the little tortoise-shell colored fury off my arm and sat Munchie on the bed, but the feline immediately jumped off the king-sized duvet and was back pawing my arm. As Alice made another attempt to capture the kitty, the trauma of the sickness flooded over me in a dark wave of exhaustion.

'Second' to a Pirate

I looked up, expecting to see the lattice roof of the patio, but instead saw a stranger dressed in a linen shirt that was unbuttoned at the throat. His sleeves billowed out and snapped at the cuffs. His sleeveless leather vest, buttoned at the waist, was sown with wide lapels and had two small, side pockets. His pants were the soft suede color of maple syrup and the legs were tucked loosely into black knee-length boots. Most striking was the wide-brimmed leather hat with a short, flat crown perched on black hair with shiny ringlets. He was close shaven except for the thick black mustache.

I almost didn't notice as his right hand reached to his left hip, and in one smooth, practiced motion, he slid a dueling sabre from a scabbard. He extended the blade toward the sky and performed a reverential bow in my direction. His words were accented with an 's' that sounded exactly like the French actor Charles Boyer in 50s black-and-white movies.

"Monsieur," I heard him say. "Would you accept the honor as my second?"

My answer was instant and final. "No, I won't be your second, and whatever game or prank is being played on me, you should know it isn't funny."

He apologized for his frankness, and explained that he had spotted the blue-and-white scarf around my neck and assumed I was a fellow countryman. My hand went to my neck. Just then I noticed that I was dressed in clothes similar to this man's. I had stout boots, coarse, but well-tailored pants and a shirt with the slippery touch of raw silk. A pair of sheepskin gloves lay on the table with a fleur de lis emblazoned on each cuff. I was surprised, when I dropped my left hand to my side, that it did not connect with the knuckle guard of a dueling sabre. The man saw my instinctive reach for a non-existent weapon and shrugged, saying not to be concerned. His retainer would provide me with a suitable weapon, if required.

Before I could respond, the man re-sheathed his sabre, removed his hat, and with a flourish and slight bow introduced himself as Jean Laffite of Barataria Bay. His name was not unknown to me, as I had learned a good bit about him. What he wanted with me today, 200 years after his colossal defeat of the British, was unclear. It seemed to be involved with his request for me to serve as his second. He looked over his shoulder at two men huddled at a small wooden table shaded by a huge overgrown willow tree and whispered, "Those men are scurrilous liars who have openly defamed me. After refusing to withdraw their libelous charges against both myself and my brother, Pierre, they must pay with their lives in a duel under the willow."

Jean Laffite was prepared to take on both men singlehanded, but his adversaries, encumbered with British chivalry, refused to draw their blades until a proper second was located. Laffite pressed me again to accept his hand in friendship and agree to serve as his second. He assured me I would not suffer any harm as he would either defeat both men or, as his second, I could call for 'quarter' (meaning clemency or mercy) if the pirate's death should be imminent. Growing more and more mystified by my involuntary immersion in this historic drama, I demanded to know the cause of this lethal dispute.

Lafitte readjusted his hat and looked at me accusingly as he demanded, had I not heard of the Pardon of Jean Laffite and his colleagues by President James Madison? Indeed, my morning's discussion on the Battle of New Orleans had uncovered this important acknowledgement by President Madison of Lafitte's critical role in Old Hickory's victory. Andrew Jackson had written to President Madison apprising him of the pivotal role Laffite and his men had played in the defeat of the British. In recognition of Lafitte's heroism and patriotism, putting defense of the new State of Louisiana over the defense of his own home and community of Barataria, the President of the United States had pardoned Laffite and his men from crimes committed during the previous ten years of unfettered piracy in the Gulf of Mexico. I nodded and confirmed that I knew of the pardon.

The two gentlemen Laffite intended to challenge were adamant that the pirate had played no part in Andrew Jackson's battle. In fact, these antagonists had asserted that Lafitte had played no role in the battle at all and had bought his presidential pardon with the treasure accumulated from

193

raiding the Spanish and British ships plying the Gulf waters. Lafitte had called the two men liars and cornered them in the Fleur de Lis where they were distributing pamphlets demeaning the pirate's role in the battle.

The antagonists also alleged that Lafitte and his brother, Pierre, had been in the service of the British Navy for three months prior to the actual fight. Unwilling to withdraw their libelous charges and leave the city, the two men had taken Lafitte up on his challenge of a duel to the death. The men believed that 'two swords were better than one,' and were confident of the outcome. They would indeed fight Lafitte on his own disadvantaged terms, but only if he could secure a second to stand by in case of his certain injury or death.

When Lafitte asked me if I believed there was any truth in the defamatory claims about his loyalties, I assured him that I did not. I told him that he should also take comfort knowing that newspapers in every city in the U.S. told the true story of Jean Lafitte and his Barataria Bay pirates.

A Pirate Victory

Lafitte knew that Jackson had become a household name after the General's decisive victory over the British on the Chalmette Battlefield, and Jackson never forgot that he owed his victory at Chalmette to a pirate named Lafitte. He notified the Louisiana legislature, the U.S. Congress, and President Madison of the heroic actions of Jean Lafitte and his privateers and affirmed the pirate's true loyalties to the young republic. Jackson also knew that the British Naval Commander had offered Lafitte British citizenship for all his privateers and land of their choice in exchange for assistance in the battle against Jackson that would make the British 'sure winners.' New Orleans was undefended, and the British had more than 10,000 armed marines ready to fight.

British Admiral Cochrane reminded Lafitte that the pirate was no longer guaranteed sanctuary since Louisiana had become a U.S. state. In fact, the pirate's brother, Pierre, was already a prisoner in New Orleans, and the new Louisiana Governor vowed to secure the harbor in Barataria and expel Lafitte's men from their pirate estate. With all these facts in his favor, the British Admiral was certain that the pirate and his men would side with the British.

The British were wrong about Jean Lafitte. He did not accept their bribe. Nor did he accept their assertion of certain victory due to overwhelming superiority of force and experienced leadership. The pirate had walked the streets of New Orleans while the British juggernaut lay off shore and had seen that Jackson could barely muster 1000 ragged townspeople and a few militiamen to stand in the way of certain defeat. Even though the British had superior forces, Lafitte had already met Jackson face-to-face and calculated that Jackson standing in front of a ragtag band of musket-loading misfits was worth 10,000 British Redcoats that had never fought a single battle in the Louisiana swamp. Jackson was a leader who understood men, and Lafitte was a leader who understood the swamps. Lafitte calculated that if Jackson could convince his patchwork army to dig in behind the Rodriguez Canal and hold their ground behind huge stacks of cotton bales, Lafitte could deliver the killing stroke to the redcoats.

In order to accomplish his part of the plan, Lafitte would double-cross Admiral Cochrane. First Lafitte shook hands with Admiral Cochrane but revealed the Admiral's attack plan to Jackson. The British intended to take New Orleans by water instead of by land. With this information, Jackson dispersed his flotilla of gunboats into Lakes Borgne and Pontchartrain, thus closing the waterways and forcing the battle onto the banks of the Mississippi at Chalmette.

The British were forced to come inland below the Rodriguez Canal. The land was only as wide as a few football fields and was bordered on the left by the Mississippi River and on the right by an impenetrable alligator-infested swamp. Second, Lafitte ordered his 48 pirate cannons into position on the far side of the Mississippi directly in line with the front of the Rodriguez Canal. Lafitte and Jackson and his army of irregulars were in their positions when Colonel Pakenham gave the fateful order to charge.

Lafitte's cannons decimated the British forces and won the battle for Jackson. Outnumbered, some say by ten to one, the American force had dug in on the far side of a canal that cut an eight-foot deep, fifteen-foot wide trench running from one mile inland of the Mississippi River to the impassable swamp. On January 8, 1815, the British forces marched headlong toward the Americans, having neglected to bring the ladders and bundle of sticks necessary to cross the fifteen-foot wide canal. The entire British force faced Jackson's patchwork army of Tennessee regulars, shopkeepers, bartenders, mule skinners, Choctaw Indians, and Free Men of Color. Unable to advance across the canal, the British troops jammed together as Lafitte's cannons opened fire and slaughtered the trapped redcoats. It was the worst 25 minutes in British military history. In less than half an hour, three Generals, including Packenham and seven colonels, were dead, along with 2,000 other casualties. It seems odd, after this ignominious defeat, that British history considers Pakenham a great military tactical fighter and war hero.

As a result of the Battle of New Orleans, another 500 British soldiers turned themselves in as prisoners. General Andrew Jackson's losses were minimal. Out of 2500 Jackson militia, the American forces buried only seven of its own and had 65 wounded. It was an unparalleled victory for the young United States and made Andrew Jackson the hero of the War of 1812. His victory was Lafitte's victory, as well. Jackson had no difficulty obtaining a Presidential pardon for Jean Lafitte, his brother, Pierre, and the entire cadre of privateers who were free to walk the streets of New Orleans without fear of being arrested.

The two men accusing Jean Laffite at the Fleur de Lis had now been joined by half a dozen other men who appeared to know each other. Laffite touched my arm, signaling me to follow him as he approached the group surrounding his two adversaries. My ears picked up the mixed sound of Creole-French and American-English as the two attackers were now engaged in a verbal defense of their claims. Without warning, a newcomer struck the youngest of Laffite's opponents in the shoulder, knocking him backwards into a table. The ensuing brawl ended as quickly as it started with both Lafitte's accusers being booted out onto Royal Street with a warning to leave town or suffer the consequences.

As Laffite stood with hands on both hips, I couldn't help but tell him, "With friends like these, you needn't ever worry about your reputation being besmirched."

He smiled and shook my hand, saying that he was disappointed that he had not had the opportunity to teach his two defamers a lesson by his sword. I assured him that the written words honoring his actions in the Battle of New Orleans would prove, once and for all, that the pen was mightier than the sword.

My head ached, the light shone directly in my eyes, and my stomach felt as though someone were pressing on it. As I tried to sit up, Tuffy extended her front paws to my chest in a vain effort to push me back down. Alice came over with a wet cloth for my forehead, and I gently coaxed the heavy bomber off of me. Alice said I had been out for hours and wanted to know how I felt.

Chapter 11: Churros and Smart Casual

"Anyone who believes what a cat tells him deserves all he gets." Neil Gaiman, British author

I was famished. It was getting dark, and tonight included a visit to Clancy's. Alice asked if I was up for a night out after such a brutish bout of food poisoning.

"You don't know the half of it," I laughed. I told her how I had almost fought alongside a pirate, but it was pretty clear that Alice's question was rhetorical since she was already dressed and ready to go Clancy's with or without me. She stood at the end of the bed with one hand on her hip and the unspoken word "well?" lightly framed on her lips. She had pulled her hair back and it was evident a good portion of her toiletry had been spent on her makeup. Alice loved cosmetics. Her close friend, Sarah, had retired to San Miguel after a forty-year career as a makeup artist with both MGM and Columbia Pictures. Two years ago Sarah had introduced Alice to the 'makeup secrets' of the stars. Under the deft tutelage of a master artist Alice had discovered her own hidden talent for what she described to me as "the mystery of mascara." Blessed with an unblemished complexion and a face that could pass for a teenager my Rockette girl was to me an unlikely candidate for makeup magic. Yet here she stood before me as I had seen so many times the past two years waiting for me to give her the low wolf whistle that her slightly blushed look demanded. Alice was stunning.

I remembered the first time Alice entered the MAC boutique shop in Mexico after having spent two dozen practice sessions with her makeup artist friend Sarah. The two young girls behind the counter were soon asking Alice for tips on applying blush and eyeliner. Alice had ended that little session and proudly asked me what I thought about her having achieved such competency that she was giving lessons to the cosmetics sales staff. I responded that I just thanked the lord that MAC was an international brand that had opened a studio in San Miguel. Now Alice could buy cosmetics without taking out a bank loan. Before MAC opened in Mexico, Alice would only use Oriflame products. How a Swedish company that was actually headquartered in Switzerland convinced customers to pay sixty bucks for something called Giordani Gold Bronzing Pearls or twenty-five dollars for a tiny little brush was the real mystery to me. Fortunately, the makeup scientists at MAC had figured out how to do the same thing at half the price. Once Alice discovered MAC the owner of the local Oriflame franchise probably took a cut in pay.

Telenovela Beauty

In San Miguel, Oriflame was handled by Margarita Gralia, who owned the Oriflame franchise as well as the restaurant Chocolate and Churros. This unique combination meant that in the same block on San Augustine Street, Alice could buy the most expensive blush and lipstick sold in Latin America while eating Mexico's most delicious twisted sugar dough sticks called churros.

Alice loved Margarita's churros as much as she did Café du Monde's beignets. Just like Café du Monde, Chocolate and Churros had long lines of tourists extending out the door and down the sidewalk. Weekends were the busiest as visitors waited their turn to check off the box indicating that they had eaten at Margarita Gralia's. Behind the tourists' interest in the churros was the hope of seeing, and maybe snapping a picture of, the most famous Spanish Telenovela heartthrob in the world. Margarita Gralia's performance in *Love in Custody* had made her a superstar from Patagonia to Los Angeles. Univision's ratings in the U.S. and Mexico exceeded that of the Grammy Awards on the night of the steamy, final episode when the 45-year old Margarita finally consummated her love for her best friend's teenage son. This year-long plot of a gender-reversed *Lolita* soap opera had captured the attention of a worldwide audience. The surge in viewer ratings can only be attributed to the blonde and voluptuous Margarita Gralia. Her Chocolate and Churros restaurant was festooned with sidewalk posters advertising her movies and hit television shows. Her iconic photo of a tousled-hair blonde in a loose-fitting red dress standing on one high-heeled foot as she bent over, showing her ample cleavage, to reach the shoe strap of her bent leg, had been featured on Manhattan buses and Hollywood billboards. It was also the main promotional photo for Oriflame. In fact Margarita did not seem to be much affected by the MAC competition. There were enough well-heeled and Vogue inspired Mexico City beauties visiting San Miguel each weekend to keep the Oriflame till ringing.

Having accepted my sincerest wolf whistle in recognition of her superb 'mascara magic', Alice urged me to 'speed it up' if we were going to get to Clancy's on time. Alice had struggled more with obtaining reservations at Clancy's than she had with any other venue on our journey. The problem was not related to our kitties. Clancy's relies on its own in-house system that consists of a Garden District telephone number. Alice obtained the number and had added it to her iPhone for speed dialing. During the four weeks preceding our departure, Alice had made numerous attempts to get through to the reservation number. Each call from Mexico cost a $1.10 to hear an answering machine's response, "Clancy's is not taking reservations at this time." Thirty-three dollars into the project, Alice finally made human contact.

Taken by surprise when a human answered the phone, Alice had inadvertently begun her conversation with a reference to the illegitimate birth of the man on the other end. Whether or not this influenced his decision to report that there were no tables available until Thanksgiving was unclear. To me it seemed reasonable to assume a conversation starting with the words *"you bastards"* might end badly. Alice had slammed down her iPhone swearing that she would get us into Clancy's. And so she had, as I was about to find out.

Alice supervised my choice of clothes for this night out at a 'smart casual' restaurant. She shook her head when I reached for my Kirkland jeans. She knew I enjoyed wearing them without a belt in order to reveal the waistband labeled '34.' Actually, this pair was a '36', but some underpaid garment worker in Malaysia had attached the wrong label. Instead, she pointed to a pair of slacks, indicating that my evening would be spent in a pair of freshly pressed Docker khakis. Before I could even unfold my favorite Jack Daniels Black T-shirt, Alice tossed me a blue, pinpoint, long-sleeved oxford dress shirt that she had secretly slipped into my 'all beach, all the time' wardrobe. I dressed in my Sigma Chi frat-house uniform of chinos, blue oxford, long-sleeved shirt, and navy blazer with brass buttons. Now I understood why Alice had insisted on my packing a pair of Bass Weejun penny loafers that I had not worn in almost three years.

Alice Makes her Mark

Tuffy was meowing; Munchie was huffing. Alice was radiant. We headed for the front door of the Monteleone carrying two cats in carriers. As expected, the dinner hour was turning out couples dressed in every imaginable style. Men chatting on their phones wore cargo shorts and polos, while their mates primped in front of hand mirrors while waiting in the taxi line. Our Uber ride was still five minutes away.

Standing at the top of three inlaid steps at the Monteleone's front door, we had a clear view over the queue ahead. Alice passed Munchie's carrier to me as she rummaged in her Nino Bossi Boogie-Woogie shoulder bag for her iPhone. Heads turned toward my Alice, who continued to grope in her bag, oblivious to the attention she drew. Smartly attired in her striped Isabel Pedro that was perfectly accented by her Phillip Plein heels and a striking shoulder bag, Alice was the epitome of 'smart casual.'

Alice turned toward the concierge desk. "Ha," she scoffed, sending my eyes back in the same direction. Standing beside it with her hands on her hips was a California blonde wearing a sparkling, spaghetti-strap top that clung like Saran Wrap to her yoga-toned frame. Her skin-tight stretch capris almost touched the gladiator laces winding up her ankles from her four-inch black, open-toe stiletto heels.

"Is that 'smart casual'?" I whispered.

"No, that's slutty, and screams, 'I will not be going to Clancy's,'" Alice said, tugging me down the stairs and out to our waiting Uber driver.

The road to Clancy's is long and winding. The uptown stretch of the road is on Annunciation Street which runs parallel to the Audubon Zoo for a few blocks. That explained why Clancy's is said to be located in the 'Audubon' neighborhood. The house that was featured in the movie, *Benjamin Button,* was in this neighborhood. Anne Rice lived nearby for many years, just down the street from where Archie Manning and his wife had raised two star, quarterback sons: Peyton and Eli. Sean Penn had bought Helen Mirrens' house on Audubon Street, and John Goodman stops for barbecue at the Voodoo bar while walking his daughter to Audubon Park for soccer practice. Bob Dylan keeps adding on to his Audubon Park manse, and

Nicolas Cage is, comparatively speaking, a 'slum landlord' with his three mansions tucked away within walking distance of Clancy's.

In addition to the full and part-time celebrity residents of the town, the city is the backdrop for as many as ten movies a year starring many of Hollywood's A-list actors. They, along with many recognizable sports figures and politicians, visit this neighborhood regularly. It's not surprising to spot someone with a famous face on any night of the week at Clancy's. Quite possibly, the star quotient of this neighborhood bistro was a prime reason for its popularity with so many New Orleans visitors. Good food is the town's major export, and visitors flying in from St. Paul or Eugene are likely to look for a reservation along with a chance to dine beside Sandra Bullock.

Clancy's vs. RTs

Hobnobbing with celebrities was not our purpose in choosing Clancy's. We would not be shocked to see a recognizable face but that was not our reason for going there. Alice and I fully expected the restaurant to live up to its reputation as the Creole bistro that started the New Orleans Creole dining scene. We would be surprised if the *Fried Oysters and Brie* or *Smoked, Soft-Shell Cra*b didn't live up to its fame. We had another reason - a more personal reason for choosing Clancy's. We were going to have a contest. You might say 'an eat off'. Alice and I planned to measure Clancy's against RT's, our own long-time favorite Creole neighborhood bistro where men seldom showed up in blue blazers but the women were all dressed as 'smart casual.' Tonight was the ultimate Bistro Creole Neighborhood Restaurant Challenge between the internationally recognized, New Orleans King of Creole Cooking: Clancy's and our favorite Creole spot in Alexandria, VA, Queen of Cajun Cuisine: RT's.

This would be a scored battle. Alice and I would award points for food, drinks and ambiance on a weighted scale from one to five, where five was the highest score and one was the lowest. In order to get this monumental challenge under way, we first had to make it past Clancy's front door. Could we walk into Clancy's with two cats in carriers hanging from our shoulders? We had made it through RT's door on our first try. How would we be received at Clancy's? Quite possibly, the contest would end before it started. More likely, we would be ushered directly to our reservation table. After all, Sandra Bullock always brought her Persian cat, Tiffany, with her, and we had seen photos of Nicholas Cage feeding filet to his Westy at Clancy's corner-window table.

Before entering the front door Alice halted and insisted we should give Clancy's a high score on curb appeal and signage. Alice pointed out the word "Clancy's" was splayed across one of the two plate-glass windows guarding each side of the entrance. Alice had taken careful note of the bright red font with upward slanting strokes and recognized it as the Lucinda Calligraphy font she had used on her business stationery for years. She was about to give Clancy's a five and an automatic 'win' for this decorative choice until I reminded her that RT's was not devoid of stylistic signage. I reminded Alice that the bent and rusted metal awning running across the front of our Arlandria spot had been replaced by a new awning with the words "RT's Restaurant" spelled out in pure, white, Times New Roman. Perhaps Clancy's should get a point more for the fancy calligraphy but there was one more element to consider. RT's also had the narrow pencil-shaped neon sign attached to the roof that displayed RT's vertically in a warm blue glow. Alice considered my comparisons and said 'touché,'. We agreed to a tie on the signage.

On looks and location, we completely disagreed. Alice thought Clancy's shiplap-wood gray siding on the renovated two-story house along with its convenient corner location, outscored RT's. She would not accept my argument that RT's one-story white brick exterior on the end of a sidewalk storefront on Mt. Vernon Avenue was no less appealing than Clancy's 1930s rehabbed family home in uptown New Orleans. Alice harrumphed and reminded me that RT's early Apache decorated exterior was squeezed in next door to a 'Cambio de Cheque' and a 'Shear Illusion' hair salon. I insisted that many women would consider the convenience of being able to cash a paycheck and get their hair done before dining at RT's a really big plus factor. Rather than argue, Alice agreed to a tie on location and looks.

Of course, there was also the doorway and entrance of each restaurant to compare. Alice ran her hand down Clancy's antique-finished Jeld Wen double doors that were fitted with ten clear panes on each side. This elegant entry offered arrivals like us a first glimpse into Clancy's whitewashed interior before opening the door. The entrance was also inviting and friendly. "Top that," she challenged me.

When it came to doors, I knew that RT was deficient. Its single-panel, brown-stained, fake mahogany was embellished with a narrow speakeasy window at eye level. When approaching the door, we had always expected a bouncer to pop his head out and yell, "What's the secret word?" Opening and closing the door was assisted by a secondhand hydraulic arm fitted across the inside that was generally out of order. During the winter, new arrivals opened the door to a chorus of "close the dang door!" as the chilled wind whistled directly into the open bar area. Reluctantly, I agreed that in our scoring system, Clancy's earned a five over RT's two points for overall curb appeal.

As we entered Clancy's, a tuxedo-clad server standing beside the bar walked over carrying a notepad scrawled with reservation names. Alice pointed to our name

205

highlighted in yellow. Without a comment about our plus-two in tow, the server guided us up three steps to what was known as the Upper Room. The Lower Room was sort of L-shaped with the bar in the narrow leg of the L and the dining area spilling out around it. We both noticed the brilliant white table linen with crystal and silverware laid out on each table. "Brentwood chairs," I whispered to Alice as our server showed us to Nicolas and Westy's usual table beside the street facing window.

Our server immediately asked if we had a favorite beverage or wanted to look over the house cocktails first. We took the handwritten house-cocktail menu for perusal and our server slipped away. So far, a certain ambiance came through that appealed to my sense of dining pleasure. By now, Alice had both kitties situated on the two spare chairs that remained pushed under our table and tented under the white linen tablecloth.

"Brentwood." Alice repeated my words back to me. "These are the exact style of chairs we sat in last night at Gautreau's. And check out the table settings." The centerpiece candles had a familiar look.

"Don't you see?" Alice implored. "It's a dinner party scene like at Gautreau's, except here it's in 'smart casual' rather than 'upscale elegance.'"

I took her point. Clancy's had a very clubby dinner party feeling, but a dinner party nonetheless. Alice enjoyed my amused look at absorbing this rather obvious comparison between the two restaurants whose menus could not have been more different. I asked Alice what she knew about this stylistic similarity between the two venues.

"The moment I saw the interior photos of the two restaurants on their respective websites, I knew. That was how I confirmed the reservation." Alice touched her finger to her temple and told me about the last phone call she had made to Clancy's restaurant owner. She had called him at home and caught him off guard. Identifying herself only as a web blogger reviewing dining venues in New Orleans, she had honestly reported that she would be at Gautreau's and wondered if Clancy's could fit her in if she promised an unbiased review of the two establishments. All he responded with was, "What time and what name?" I blew her a little kiss to congratulate her for her competitive thinking. The two must-visit venues might convey a relaxed nonchalance about their respective positions in the New Orleans restaurant food chain, but underneath the white aprons, they would scratch tooth and nail to beat each other at an 'unbiased' review.

Settling back with the house-cocktail menu, I was intrigued by the drink marked as Clancy's Sazerac and told Alice it looked like it was time to try the city's most famous drink. Supposedly the first cocktail in America, the Sazerac had what some would call a 'refined taste.' As long as it was properly made with rye whiskey, it could be called anything they liked, as far as my taste was concerned. The Sazerac was not my choice of an everyday beverage, but there would never be a more appropriate time to try one than here in the city where the very name 'cocktail' was invented, and the first cocktail was a Sazerac.

A New Orleans apothecary named Antoine Peychaud is credited with originating both the name and the drink. After 170 years, the most popular brand of bar bitters in the world is still Peychaud's. Antoine Peychaud's bitters were a secret blend of ingredients that he splashed into French brandy to add the "bitter" taste. Antoine prepared these high-percent alcohol concoctions using a double-sided eggcup, much like the double- sided jiggers used in bars today.

Alice told me that the double-sided eggcups were known by their French name, 'coquetier' or 'kokotay,' that in true American fashion became 'cocktail.' Some bars still use brandy as the base liquor in the Sazerac, but the American version uses Bulleit Rye, which blends well with Peychaud's bitters.

At home I keep a bottle of Pernod as a substitute for the Herbsaint or Absinthe that is typically used to start the drink. I also use the simple syrup rather than a sugar cube to assure the right amount of sweetness. Judging from the cocktail menu, it appeared that Clancy's had its own version of this classic cocktail. Our server was prompt and after taking my order for a Sazerac and Alice's for a Kentucky Mule, presented us with the handwritten menus for that night's dinner. Alice asked how I thought Clancy's stacked up in the hospitality category.

"Couldn't be higher," I said, not bothering to mention that we received this sort of personal attention every time we visited RT's, even without claiming to be a restaurant critic. Two more tuxedo-clad servers appeared to attend to the ever-growing number of guests funneling into the main dining room from the front doors. In my navy-blue blazer and khaki chinos, I blended perfectly with the crowd spreading out among the tables. My age group was well represented, and there were more brass-buttoned blazers on the clientele than on the USC Trojans' marching band. The women clearly knew the definition of 'smart casual,' and if a scantily dressed female should appear, the management would probably hand her a shawl.

Two more couples followed our server up the steps to take up seats at nearby tables. The way he led them through the aisles while balancing our drinks on a small tray reminded me of the movie, *Around the World in 80 Days*. With his starched shirt and thin mustache, our server bore a remarkable resemblance to David Niven's companion, the versatile and funny Cantinflas.

"No Pappy's, only Woodford Reserve", were our server's first words as he sat the chilled, copper mug in front of Alice. Score a five for RT's, I registered on my mental scoreboard while checking to make sure that Alice got the message. RT's substituted with Maker's Mark which was

Alice's preferred. Clancy's substituted Woodford – another fine bourbon but not as good a match for Alice's flavor spot.

As he set down the Clancy's Sazerac, I asked, "What makes it a Clancy's Sazerac?"

"We swish with Pernod rather than Herbsaint, and always use simple syrup instead of sugar cubes."

I smiled. "Another point for Clancy's," I whispered noting that the bar used Pernod and simple syrup - just like at home. Alice and I toasted our clubby new dining spot.

I took a moment to score the bout. So far it looked like a virtual tie between Clancy's and RT's. Clancy's scored well on location and looks while RT's had the advantage on a more flexible dress code. They tied on hospitality, attention and house cocktails even though Clancy's did not have Pappy Van Winkle for Alice's Kentucky Mule. But they did make the perfect Sazerac.

Alice and I agreed that wine lists would not be part of the judging criteria. Great wine, of course, compliments great cuisine, but nothing makes up for bad food. We never considered ourselves wine snobs and we were only slightly beyond the 'red goes with meat and white goes with fish,' stage of understanding the nuances of wine lists. But the wine list at Clancy's put the one at the Ritz-Carlton in Laguna Niguel to shame. For a cozy neighborhood restaurant, the only thing missing at Clancy's was a sommelier to help the clientele make the right choice. Alice and I both prefer white bourgogne, and she pointed out the list included a favorite of ours in the well-priced *Bouchard Pere et Fils Reserve*. This was the same white bourgogne we first tasted so many years ago at the Relais Odeon in Paris. I reminded Alice that RT's sometimes keeps this on tap in their 'by the glass' wine cooler, along with three or four selections of the week so we had to score Clancy's and RT's even on this metric.

Turning serious attention to the dinner menu, I asked Alice for her opinion on the choices we should make in order to have a fair comparison to RT's. Having dined at RT's countless times during our married life, Alice and I had a fairly good feel for the entire menu. My eyes were drawn to *Clancy's Fried Oysters and Brie* starter for comparison with RT's Creole version of *Jack Daniels Shrimp*. Alice was flicking her menu at me while raising her eyebrows; this was her signal for, "Don't look now, but steal a glance at who's coming up the stairs."

Executing my best chair reshuffle, I turned slightly to find myself staring straight into James Carville's eyes. He smiled that big lopsided grin at us while he passed the table and drawled out, "How's y'all's evenin' going?" as he sat down with two colleagues, both of whom were dressed in business attire: pin-striped suits, regimental striped ties and cap-toed Florsheim lace-up shoes. Carville, however, was wearing a pair of Nike-emblazoned track pants, New Balance trainers and a pocket polo shirt with a little shark embroidered on the pocket. So much for 'smart-casual.' Alice held her finger to her lips, warning me to stop laughing. How perfect, I thought. America's most famous political strategist arrives at Clancy's for a business dinner dressed in what any male would describe as a man's 'smart casual,' while all around him, his brethren are suited up for a front-row fraternity picture. How would we score this one?

I turned to Alice saying, "If we had a celebrity score, Clancy's deserves a five for hosting the political genius and famous commentator who got an Arkansas governor into the highest office in the land." James Carville was also known worldwide for his Cajun accent, his scoffing laugh, squinty eyes and engaging lopsided grin.

"How could RT's top that?" I smugly inquired, already knowing the answer.

210

Celebrity Diners at RT's

"Not so fast," Alice said. I knew where she was going with this. While Clancy's hosted the man who got Bill Clinton elected, we had been at RT's when RT's had hosted the man, himself.

One Thursday night in November shortly after the 1996 Presidential election, we had settled into our usual booth at RT's when a row of black-window tinted Suburbans pulled up at the curb and unloaded a dozen muscled men in dark suits, red ties and earphones not-too-discreetly shoved into their ears. Swiftly and without objection, they moved everyone at the tables to the bar side of the restaurant where we were already comfortably sitting in a booth. Twenty minutes later, a motorcade with lights flashing rolled down Mt. Vernon Avenue and stopped in front of the door which was guarded by two (un-secretive) secret service men. In strode the new President, Bill Clinton, followed by his new Vice President, Al Gore.

The Vice President was no stranger to RT's, and we had dined at our little hideaway at tables adjacent to him, his wife Tipper and his kids, Sarah and Albert, several times while he was still the Senator from Tennessee. Tipper Gore's family owned a roomy but unpretentious colonial, center hall-styled home near Ridge Road in Arlington, only a few blocks away from Arlandria and RT's. After the election, the new Vice President had invited the President to join him for dinner at his favorite Creole spot nestled in the Arlandria valley.

Two plates with artist's caricatures of the politicians hung from the dining-room ceiling cornice to commemorate the occasion. RT's used dinner plates with famous diner's caricatures to memorialize famous visitors, whereas Clancy's commemorated such guests with a row of pencil-sketched drawings.

211

"If we were going to award scores based on celebrity diners, who would win this contest," I asked Alice?

"RT's for sure," she said, and pointed down at Munchie's carrier still sitting unobtrusively beneath the tablecloth. "Don't forget," she added. "In addition to the two plates with Bill and Al's faces, there is also the plate with a cat's face."

She was right. At RT's, beside the two plates with grease-pencil sketches of Clinton and Gore, hung a serving saucer with a masterfully executed sketch of the most perfect kitty that had ever lived on earth.

I couldn't hold back a wide grin as Alice reminded me of the night we had arrived early at RT's without knowing about Bill and Al's dinner plans. Our favorite bartender, Lynn, had called Alice earlier in the day and told us to come early because RT's would be closed to all visitors after 7:00 p.m. due to a special function. We showed up with our purebred Maine Coon named OJ riding in a sling that was draped from Alice's neck. OJ was pale yellow, like the pale-colored liquid from a ripening spring fruit, and was just as sweet. Hence his name.

When Alice first approached RT's owner about making the restaurant "cat friendly" (at least for OJ), she received immediate agreement. Our longstanding status as unabashed fans of RT's with an open purse may have tipped the scales in OJ's favor. Our affectionate little guy had enjoyed his excursions to RT's where he could pop his head out of the sling to search for a welcoming spot on the table where he was eager to sniff out our evening's dinner choices. RT's offerings were New Orleans-worthy in their own right, but the appetizers were so scrumptious that they must have been created from recipes handed down by Saint Martha, one of the patron saints of cooks. An OJ favorite was the *Crawfish and Shrimp Beignets* that always received a dainty sniff or two. He especially seemed to enjoy a lick of the *Arcadian Pepper Shrimp* or the *Oysters-Three-Way*. At times, we skipped entrees and dined exclusively on starters. OJ always preferred the appetizers to the entrée, except when we ordered the *Shellfish in Parchment*. As soon as the parchment was torn open, the exquisite aroma of shrimp, scallops and lump crabmeat drew OJ out of his sling like the proverbial fly to honey. OJ would nibble at the lump crab, lick the scallops, but sneer at the shrimp.

Alice and OJ had been literally inseparable. At home, OJ never left Alice's side to wander off and explore in the back closet or look under the bed upstairs. His nickname was 'Necklace.' At night, he slept on Alice's pillow, wrapped around her head. During the evenings, while Alice hammered away on her computer, the pale-yellow kitty would drape himself around her neck like a feathered boa.

OJ was only ten-weeks old when he had been introduced to Alice. I had brought him home from the Arlington Shelter as a surprise gift. Alice had been ill and had been fading away in front of my very eyes. I didn't know how to cure her. Her illness had started out as a tickle in her throat. She left for work and kept her appointments with the bureaucrats. Returning home long after dark, her throat was on fire as she dragged herself up the back stairs with a wet, hacking cough. Sedated with Cold-EEZE, she collapsed into a deep slumber. By morning, she couldn't get out of bed. Seven-Up and toast were the only foods she would accept. Her condition worsened until the fifth day when I bundled her in a quilt and drove her to our family physician's office. He diagnosed her with severe bronchitis, pre-pneumonia and urged me to keep her rested with lots of fluids, aspirin and an antibiotic he prescribed. Privately, he told me the Rockette girl was severely depressed.

I was not surprised. LeRoy had died a week before her symptoms had appeared. He had been with Alice from high school through college and grad school. From the first night I met LeRoy on the bed in Alice's Dupont Circle apartment, he had accepted me as an equal for Alice's affection. Even when LeRoy's health was failing, Alice refused to let him go. He was in his 20s, and with his kidneys failing and his oversized, tuxedo-clad body bulging with excess fluids, we made daily trips to the vet's for dialysis treatments. After two weeks of drainage and IVs, Alice decided that she had to let LeRoy go. She realized that it was cruel to keep him alive by putting him through the daily treatments. She held him as the vet administered the final IV.

Seven days passed since leaving our doctor's office with a diagnosis of severe depression and bronchitis, and Alice continued sleeping. Her diet of 7-Up and toast was now reduced to just the soft drink. I lay beside her each night as she struggled to find the words to say that she would be better tomorrow, but tomorrow came and went and my Rockette girl continued wasting away. She refused to return to the doctor, and after the fifteenth day, I drove to a shelter.

Alice was asleep, breathing heavily, with curtains drawn against the afternoon sun. The room was totally dark when I slipped in with the tiny yellow fur ball whose bright, orange eyes occupied half his face. Without waking her from her dreams, I deposited the squirming creature in the crook of her arm, and backpedaled out of the room. At the time, her closet still held LeRoy's box and his Hello Kitty bowl containing the last bits of hard IAMs. My night was spent on the sofa, wrapped in a blanket, expecting at any moment to hear Alice awaken with a shout. Morning broke to find me tossing off the quilt as I heard the kettle singing in the kitchen. I ran to the door to find Alice sitting on the bar stool, swathed in her fluffy white bathrobe, her hands tucked down in the robe's wide pockets from which a little yellow blob with two orange eyes peeked out at the whistling sound.

Alice teared up and said, "I will never forget LeRoy." She removed the kettle from the stove and put it on a nearby trivet. "This one's name is OJ," she said as she pulled the wriggly little kitty out of her pocket and held him for me to inspect. My Rockette girl was back.

"'OJ,' for sure," I said, pouring the kettle's piping-hot water into her teacup. Alice eventually recovered her appetite, and OJ never lost his. Within one year, OJ had a thick lion's mane, and shaggy bloomers that swished against his back legs. He was smaller than LeRoy but twice as affectionate. OJ loved humans, and of all humans, he loved Alice best. OJ never willingly left Alice's side when she was in the house, and soon Alice was taking OJ to work in a custom-made sling with deep folds, a screen and a zipper. He scrunched the folds with his paws, and always found a comfortable position. It was unclear whether OJ thought he was a furry four-footed human, or if Alice and I were furless, two-footed cats. Either way, OJ knew he was the king, and our job was to dance to his tune.

Like all kitties, OJ enjoyed his rest. But unlike other kitties, OJ liked to play every moment he was awake. More importantly, OJ expected his humans to join him in play. He didn't require a cloth mouse with catnip, a colorful ball, or even a piece of string; a shoelace, lampshade, drapery cord, orange peel, door key or even a garage door opener provided endless fun. He always expected the nearest human to chase or follow him as he batted, shoved and fought imaginary foes. OJ loved nothing better than standing on a pair of shoes that had human feet inside. With claws outstretched, he would begin to climb the tree-like leg. Pants, skirts, ball gowns, and tuxedos were all just pathways to the stars or, in OJ's case, the neck. OJ preferred Alice's neck but would settle for the neck and shoulders of any human if Alice were not available. OJ never met a human he didn't love, and we never met a human who could resist picking up the fluffy yellow lion with the super-long whiskers.

OJ's overt friendliness only became a drawback once Alice started taking him out to dinner with us. As long as he was in the sling, OJ was content to stretch and tug and claw on the shawl to persuade Alice to free him. Once out of the sling on his flexible little leash, OJ didn't stray but was sure to take over the table. He could make everyone watching smile as he walked the tightrope of the table's edge.

OJ Meets the President

The night President Clinton and Vice President Gore entered RT's, our little yellow fireball was tiptoeing around the edge of our booth, intently watching Lynn fill up the salt and pepper shakers. When the Clinton-Gore team arrived, OJ was pondering the salt and pepper shakers on the serving table. As the crowd on the inside of the dining area 'oohed' and 'awed' at the arrival of special guests, we wondered if there were as many secret service outside RT's as inside. One of the men adjusted his little earpiece and took up a watchful pose beside our booth and next to my left shoulder, which completely blocked my view at the end of the wine bar.

It was, coincidently, at the end of the bar where the other patrons saw a large, pale-yellow kitty. He had, somehow, managed to wiggle out of his collar and was watching everything with great interest. As Alice held up the leash attached to an empty collar, she gasped as she realized that OJ had escaped. We turned toward the bar where Lynn was pointing 'that-a-way' in the direction of the dining room. Alice jumped from the booth and the man with the earplug instinctively plopped two ham-sized hands on top of her shoulders, not realizing that no one and nothing could stop Alice when she was worried about her kitty.

Alice dragged the secret service agent around the corner of the booth where I stood, craning my neck to see over the partition into the dining room. Six men arranged around the center table surrounded Vice President Gore who was shouting, "What the heck?" upon discovering that a certain kitty had hopped onto his shoulders, which provided twice the area of Alice's neck. Alice pushed her way into the party in an attempt to rescue both the cat and the Vice President.

216

Upon seeing her with her hands outstretched, Vice President Gore turned his back so Alice could peel OJ off his shoulders without causing any more damage to his suit. I watched the room burst into laughter as four men in blue suits returned their weapons to inside their jackets.

Alice stood at the table apologizing while the President said not to worry, that they had been attacked by a lot worse during the campaign. Two secret service agents escorted Alice and OJ back to our bar side table while Lynn helped trap OJ within Alice's sling shawl.

OJ was so agitated, and Alice so shaken, that we had no choice but to leave our Kentucky Mule and Vieux Carre untouched on the table. The following week when we dined at RT's, there were three new plates on the wall: one for Clinton, one for Gore and one for OJ.

The boisterous laughter coming from the Carville party brought me back to Clancy's where my hand instinctively reached to confirm Tuffy's presence in the carrier under the table. Mr. Carville burst out with another of his booming guffaws that seemed to always accompany his comments on television. Our server used this occasion to approach us with suggestions for our order. Alice was determined to sample the *Fried Oysters and Brie* while I was just as committed to the *Shrimp Remoulade* appetizer. Alice said, "Why not try the *Crawfish Vol-au-Vent* instead of the shrimp?"

I was torn, because any Creole restaurant willing to put together a vol-au-vent deserves to have their pastry mastery recognized. If Clancy's had been serving a shrimp vol-au-vent, I would definitely have wanted to try their version of a shrimp-filled pastry with creamy dill sauce. But tonight's vol-au-vent was with crayfish, and it didn't seem fair to compare a crayfish creation to a shrimp creation from RT's. Instead, I chose the *Shrimp Remoulade* so Alice and I could compare the two Cajun sauces.

Alice said, "It's ridiculous and a waste to miss out on Clancy's special offerings just to satisfy some imaginary competition." She had a point, but I stuck with the *Shrimp Remoulade*.

Having overheard us, our waiter politely asked if he could make a suggestion as long we were doing a comparison of Creole menus. Alice and I welcomed his attention, and filled him in on our attempt to compare our own favorite Creole spot back in Arlington, Virginia, with Clancy's.

He smiled and said, "The best dish for such a taste test would be the *Crawfish Etouffee*, as every Creole kitchen offers this dish but no two are exactly alike." It sounded like a good idea, so I ordered the *Crawfish Etouffee* and selected the *Soft Shell Crab* as an appetizer. Alice said she didn't know how authentically Creole it was, but she was not going to miss out on Clancy's *Lobster Risotto* under any circumstances. We ordered *Fried Oysters and Brie*, *Shrimp Remoulade* and the *Soft Shell Crab*, followed by *Crawfish Etouffee* and a half order of *Lobster Risotto*.

We were only half-finished with our cocktails when the server laid out the *Fried Oysters and Brie* and promised to deliver the shrimp and soft-shell crab momentarily. I covered my Sazerac and asked for a bottle of the Bouchard white bourgogne. Our server headed back to the bar.

Alice was smiling over the exceptional service. No question about it; Clancy's service was superb. Without any sense of hovering, the wait staff seemed to anticipate our every need. From our vantage point, we could look into the lower dining area and see everyone enjoying the same quality of personalized service.

With forks at the ready, Alice and I cut into the *Fried Oysters and Brie*. One bite and I knew that the memory would last forever.

Alice said, "Clancy's scores huge on this little dish," and I agreed. This specialty was markedly different from the fried oysters at RT's where the sweet pearls came lightly crisped in a buttermilk batter, and the succulent insides melted in our mouths. Every bit as crisp and juicy, the Clancy's dish was enriched with brie beyond our taste buds' limits.

"Too rich?" I asked.

"Not for me," Alice said with the second and last oyster and a blob of melted brie speared on her fork. I sat open mouthed, almost drooling, as she swallowed the sublime combination.

I asked Alice if she would trade Clancy's *Fried Oysters and Brie* for RT's *Jack Daniels Shrimp*. She cocked her head, obviously trying to imagine the lush taste of the lump crab, lightly sautéed and stuffed into the jumbo shrimp broiled with garlic and drawn butter at RT's.

"Maybe," she said, "If you included a side of RT's *Crawfish and Shrimp Beignets* with the garlic mayonnaise."

"Oh, my lord." I had completely forgotten about the beignets. Clancy's had the *Fried Oysters and Brie* but RT's had the *Crawfish and Shrimp Beignets* with garlic mayonnaise. Alice watched as I licked my lips, making room for the bottle of Brouchard's the server was dutifully uncorking. While he poured, a new waitperson appeared with both the *Shrimp Remoulade* and the soft-shell crab. What a feast this was!

Alice breathed a, "Wow!" after her first bite of the shrimp.

"Delicious?" I asked while scooping up half a shrimp in the creamy sauce.

"Different," she responded.

I guessed the difference immediately. As our server had commented earlier, every Creole kitchen has an etouffee, but no two are alike. The same goes for remoulade sauce. Almost every chef has an astringent preference, such as lemon juice, to bring out the subtle flavors of mayonnaise paired with any sort of picante pepper. Clancy's preferred Creole mustard. It was delicious, but different from RT's whose sauce relied on hot pepper and garlic. Alice decided that her ultimate would be half an order from Clancy's and half an order from RT's. My preference was for RT's, but the cozy warmth of Clancy's could be addictive. And either remoulade would go perfectly with the Bouchard's wine.

Next was the soft-shell crab. I had forgotten this choice was a Clancy's specialty. My taste buds stung as a crispy fried crustacean was placed in front of me. Alice loved crab prepared this way and so did I. After just one bite, Clancy's version, which tasted fried and smoked, was the clear winner. I had ordered it without giving much thought to this rather famous appetizer. These were the equal of any soft shells I'd ever tasted in either Charleston or Annapolis. Alice could tell from my expression that the soft shells were something special.

She took a bite and said, "It isn't fair."

"What's not fair?" I asked.

"It's not fair that we would have to come back to New Orleans to taste this ever again." She was right. It wasn't fair.

We were enjoying our second glass of white Bourgogne when the *Lobster Risotto* and *Crayfish Etouffee* were presented. The lobster was love at first bite, but we finally had a measurable difference between RT's and Clancy's when it came down to the *Crayfish Etouffee*. Clancy's serves it with a blond roux while RT's specialty is a dark roux. Both consist of butter and flour cooked in a hot skillet, preferably an iron one. The flavor changes with the cooking time, and the time to make a dark roux requires a different level of concentration and attention to the skillet temperature than does a blond roux. Clancy's roux was picture perfect. We couldn't see a black spec indicating an overcooked or overheated skillet, but a blond roux on crayfish just didn't seem right to me. On this Alice agreed, although she said the flavor was absolutely divine. While the *Crayfish Etouffee* was mouth-wateringly delicious, the blond

220

roux had something missing. Alice also reminded me that one item lacking on Clancy's menu that would really pair well with their etouffee was RT's *Corn Maque Choux*. Not only would a Louisiana succotash complement the etouffee, but it would be a perfect side order for Clancy's red meat dishes. RT's tended to soften up their version of corn maque choux with a nice mix of oil, cream and bacon drippings that infused the corn and green peppers, but I bet that Clancy's could create a Michelin three-star maque choux. As for the *Lobster Risotto*, let it be said that Clancy's does not skimp on lobster. These chunky pieces of meat in a half order would have been a full meal on the mean streets of Boston.

Tonight would be the first time Alice and I did not join the clean plate club, but we had to leave room for the *Ice Box Lemon Pie*. Bits of lobster were already being slipped into Tuffy's carrier under the table, and Munchie had been licking the butter off my fingers ever since the drinks arrived.

If Alice could choose only one dessert for life, it would be key lime pie. After tasting Clancy's *Ice Box Lemon Pie*, that list now includes two choices. It was time to vote. Who would take home the blue ribbon for favorite Creole dining spot. Would it be Clancy's, the 'King of Creole Bistros', or RT's, the 'Queen of Cajun Cuisine'?

I looked to Alice for any last considerations before we paid our check; price was never to be part of our decision. Alice turned up her chin in a thoughtful look and reviewed the contenders. We had looks and location and hospitality attention, food, and ambiance.

"There is one thing more." she said. I wondered what we could have missed or how we could even make this decision. "Just one thing," she repeated. "OJ never danced on the tables at Clancy's."

Although a bit prejudiced, my Rockette girl was right. The win went to RT's for allowing "catdancing".

John Folse's Recipe for Remoulade (RT's Style)

One and a half cups heavy mayonnaise
Half a cup Creole mustard
1 tbsp. Worcestershire sauce
One half a cup catsup
1 tsp. hot pepper sauce (Chef Folse likes Louisiana Gold, but Tabasco will do)
One half a cup finely diced green onions
One quarter cup finely diced celery
2 tbsp. minced garlic
One quarter cup finely chopped parsley
One half tbsp. lemon juice
Salt and cracked black pepper to taste
3 dozen, 21-25-count boiled shrimp, peeled and deveined

In a mixing bowl, combine all of the above ingredients, whisking well to incorporate the seasonings. Once blended, cover and refrigerate, preferably overnight. A minimum of four hours is required for flavor to be developed. When ready, remove from refrigerator and adjust seasonings to taste. Place six shrimp on a leaf of romaine or other colored lettuce, and spoon a generous serving of remoulade sauce on top. Do not sauce shrimp prior to service, as they will lose their firm texture.

Corn Maque Choux (RT's)

2 tbsp. (One half a stick) butter
1 cup finely chopped onion
One half a cup chopped red bell pepper
2 cups fresh corn kernels (cut from 3 medium ears of corn)
One half a cup heavy whipping cream
1 tsp. chopped fresh thyme
One half tsp. (or more) hot pepper sauce
1 green onion, finely chopped
2 tbsp. chopped fresh Italian parsley
1 tbsp. chopped fresh basil
Coarse kosher salt

Melt butter in large skillet over medium-high heat. Add onion and sauté until translucent, about five minutes. Add bell

222

pepper; sauté until beginning to soften, about three minutes. Add corn; sauté for two minutes. Add cream, thyme, and _ tsp. hot pepper sauce. Simmer until sauce thickens, about five minutes. Mix in green onion, parsley, and basil. Season to taste with coarse salt, pepper, and more hot pepper sauce, if desired

Chapter 12: Alice Tells All

"A dog, I have always said, is prose; a cat is a poem." Jean Burden, poet

All four of us had a good night's sleep. By checkout time, we were on the Pascagoula Bay Bridge looking at Gulfport and Biloxi in the Fit's rear-view mirror. Mobile was straight ahead, and the early start put us ahead of schedule. As morning light broke in the French Quarter, we bid adieu to the Crescent City and headed directly into the morning sun for our scheduled stopover in Atlanta. Our route took us east along the Gulf coast to Mobile, which was the entrance to Alabama's version of the Vast Wasteland. From Mobile we would be driving two hours northeast, through a rural forest of Alabama pines stretching from the coast to the Capitol. Our plan called for a short stop in Montgomery before continuing on I-85 into Atlanta.

Munchie and Tuffy seemed to be enjoying this leg of our journey much more than Alice and I were. With the iPad in front of her face, our tortoise-shell colored terror was content to sit frozen on the center console, staring at the *Song Birds of the Carolinas*. Tuffy, meanwhile, was experiencing wanderlust in the Fit, and had spent the first 150 miles snaking her way in and around the luggage and boxes.

Before leaving the New Orleans garage, Alice had assisted me in arranging the cargo so that the boxes and bags overlapped, leaving hand-sized crawl spaces running between the luggage. Now Tuffy could explore the interior using her whiskers to calculate the space needed to squirm her fat body through the different openings. Tuffy always acted as though her fat bottom were no wider than her head. Time and again, we have enjoyed watching Tuffy climb to the top of her cat tree, hand-sized hole leading into the crow's nest, only to discover she could squeeze her head and shoulders through the hole but would fail in squirming the balance of her kitty frame inside. As the Fit spun along toward Montgomery, our oversized feline was attempting to squeeze into each of the pathways Alice had created. I could only grab a glimpse now and then of a fat-bottomed cat with two furry hind legs pumping and struggling to push her body through to the other side. Alice put her fingers to her lips several times, warning me not to laugh at the determined efforts of our lap sitter to push a twenty-pound body through a fifteen-pound sized hole.

Laughing was out of the question unless I wished to have a huge black fur ball hop onto my lap. Tuffy was sensitive. She was easily embarrassed and could sense when I was laughing at her rather than with her. She had once jumped onto the dinner table without realizing that Alice had lay linen place mats on the surface. Tuffy had landed on one mat, and the velocity of her jump turned the mat into a kitty sled that careened across the slick surface, slinging a totally shocked cat off the table and into cat space. She had tumbled onto her back and sprang up, looking around to see which one of us had pushed her. My riotous laughter was enough of a signal to indicate culpability, and Tuffy took two bounding hops back onto the table and onto my lap with both paws on my lips as she started her little yelping.

Alice reminded me that any laughter while driving could spark a retaliatory move. I kept quiet, but asked for the box trick to lure the fat feline out of the luggage and into a more somnambulant state. Alice unfolded the pasteboard box she kept for this occasion, and taped the bottom closed. It was a small box from Mega Grocery Store used to transport four quarts of spicy salsa and was just large enough to fit one oversized feline named Tuffy. The only spot Alice could open the box was on the floor at her feet, so she popped open the top of the box and waited for the inevitable. With a sixth sense derived from eons of cats finding boxes, our Tuffy was out of the luggage and peering into the front seat area, searching for the new play environment. All cats seem to love climbing into and out of boxes but not all cats enjoy doing what Tuffy does. Without any encouragement from Alice, our kitty measured the distance and leapt over Munchie, who was hugging the console, and landed with a fat flop directly inside the cardboard container at Alice's feet. She poked her head up long enough to see that she was half covered by the dashboard, and out of sight from any imaginary eyes in the back-cargo section. Very carefully, she stretched out. Delicately extending her right paw, she hooked the open flap of the box with a claw and pulled it up and down, closing one corner of the box. With the one partition slightly ajar, she carefully pulled the three other flaps down against the first flap and jerked the pasteboard corners down into a flat top. Our fat-bottomed girl was now safely hidden inside her own makeshift cave where she would stay until she tired of the game. She would probably sleep all the way to Montgomery, and that was fine with us. Tuffy was a kitty whose entire life had been spent around humans. In fourteen years, she had never heard a harsh word or felt anything but love from her human companions, of which Alice and I were the second and third.

Tuffy was a rescue kitty that Alice had adopted for her mother, Marge, whose health had deteriorated to the point that she required assistance in daily life. We had added a handicapped apartment to our Arlington home, complete with a walk-in tub and an eight-week-old kitten named Tuffy. Marge had been as happy as she had ever been. She cried when Alice told her she would be moving in with us. She had been self-sufficient all her life, but her crippling arthritis and leaky heart valve was robbing her of the independence she had cherished since being stricken with idiopathic juvenile arthritis during her college days in Colorado. The cruel disease left her unable to uncurl her fingers and made every move of her ankles, shoulders, elbows and knees a painful trial. When Marge learned that it was my idea to move her into our home and provide her with her own apartment, complete with kitchen, movie room and Jacuzzi, she realized that she was family.

Tuffy adopted Marge the day she moved in with us. For the next six years, the two were inseparable. Tuffy slept next to Marge and padded after her like a tiny shadow. Alice sat on the bed next to her mother during her Mom's final hours while Tuffy rested on her mother's arm. As Marge's breathing grew more and more shallow, Tuffy moved closer and closer to her face. When her breath ceased, her little companion put two chubby paws on her face. That night, I carried Tuffy upstairs to our room and put her in the bed next to my exhausted Rockette girl. Without so much as a huff from Munchie, Tuffy had been our fat-bottomed girl ever sense.

Marge's Gift from Scottie

Now we were on our way to Montgomery, Alabama, with Tuffy in a box, Munchie stalking birds and Alice leafing through the hard-copy color photos her Mom had left in her drawer. Marge had received these photocopies as a gift one Christmas from her college roommate, and Alice and I had both enjoyed studying them. Today would be the first time either of us would see the original subjects as her Mom had told us that the copies did not do the subjects justice and really deserved a firsthand look. We both agreed with Marge they deserved a firsthand look but Montgomery was not on any routes that Alice and I ever traveled. This trip would put us right in the middle of the city where we could stop and see these originals and decide for ourselves if they were as dramatic as Marge had insisted.

As much as I was looking forward to the stopover, I was concerned that a lot of sad memories might be stirred up for Alice. Except for the stoned cat incident, Alice had exhibited the contentment of a Little Miss Sunshine throughout the entire trip. Alice was smilingly optimistic with an uplifting mood. She rarely got depressed. She was a problem-solver and believed in self-determination. Since falling in love with Alice, I went to sleep each night knowing that when Alice said, "Everything is going to be all right," it would be.

There was one exception. Alice cried for her mother. Not because she missed her mother, though she did; she cried from the memories of how difficult her mother's life had been and how wonderful Alice's had been by comparison. Alice told me she didn't feel guilty that her mother had known hardship and pain, but she felt duty bound to see that her mother never felt either again as long as she could prevent it.

To me, Alice was very lucky to have had a mother who accepted such devotion, not as a duty owed but as a precious gift, undeserved but lovingly accepted. Marge knew how much she was adored and admired by her daughter and would never take advantage of it. In fact, Marge often cautioned Alice to not do so much for her. She did not want to be an invalid, incapable of managing her own affairs. It was only during those last few years that Marge could no longer resist the protective care she finally admitted she needed and that Alice insisted she deserved. Making this visit to the Montgomery house might stir up those sad memories.

Neither Alice nor I had met her mother's college roommate who had passed away almost 25 years before Marge moved in with us. The two of them, Marge and Scottie Lanahan, had kept up a weekly phone relationship up until Mrs. Lanahan's death at a fairly early age of 66 (compared to Marge, who lived to see 90). At some point after her roommate had moved to Montgomery, the two women began to plan twice yearly Senior Citizen trips together. When the first big Indian tribe casino opened in Mobile, the two friends arranged to join a gambling junket to the Island View Casino. The casino trip gave the two of them a chance to get together and visit Scottie Lanahan's family home in Montgomery.

We were on our way to the same house where Marge had stayed on her Casino trip located in a Montgomery neighborhood called Old Cloverdale. Marge had only spent a few nights at the Lanahan home, but it gave her enough time to realize that her roommate's grandfather had been an important politician and a wealthy businessman. Judge Sayre had fathered six children; the youngest was a brilliant and vivacious girl destined to become Scottie's mother.

It was while visiting her roommate, Scottie, that Marge had first seen the framed paintings hanging along the hallways of the Montgomery home. Fairy tales and nursery rhymes had been captured in a fantastic display of acrylics, oil and watercolors. Scottie took note of how enamored Marge had been with the art and had produced a set of professionally shot photocopies of Marge's favorites that Scottie sent to Marge as a Christmas gift.

Alice and her mother had a favorite among the photocopy paintings, and we had turned it into a wall poster that hung first in Marge's apartment and later in a six-foot frame in our Mexican hallway. It was a fantasy painting of the *Three Little Pigs* done in a colorful fairytale style with the piggies literally starry-eyed and dancing on a marshmallow cloud.

Marge told us she was actually surprised that her roommate had returned to live in Montgomery. During college, Scottie had told Marge that she would never return to Montgomery. She felt the town stifled her growth, and her mother's and grandfather's reputations would always keep her from finding her own way. Marge told me she was very surprised, years later, when her former roommate wrote to say that she had changed her mind and decided to return to Montgomery. She was even more surprised to learn that she intended to move into the family home in Cloverdale. Apparently, Scottie Lanahan had not only returned to live in the family homestead but had also turned it into a museum that housed the paintings that Alice and her mother loved and that we intended to see.

Scottie Lanahan had still been living in the family home when she was felled by a heart attack while asleep in her own bed. For the next 25 years, Alice's mom had kept the photocopies of the paintings carefully wrapped in an artist's preservation binder that she only brought out to show on special occasions. Now Alice was sitting in our Fit, thumbing through the photos looking for the *Three Little Pigs*.

The Three Little Pigs and The Eagles

The Sayre House looked like the sort of home an Alabama Supreme Court Justice named Anthony Dickinson Sayre would live in. A large, two-story, clapboard-frame home with a brick-sided sunroom and a line of six-pane, double-sash windows was situated in the middle of a magnificent lot. Five riser steps to the entrance were covered by a curved porch roof with a wide bow window off to the right. A couple was exiting the front porch as Alice lashed the kitties securely in their carriers and I walked around to help extract them from the car. We stood at the foot of the stairs and read the large metal sign attached to the entryway wall. Engraved in letters that had been polished to a bright sheen, it read: *Welcome to the F. Scott Fitzgerald and Zelda Sayre Fitzgerald Museum.*

As we gazed at the plaque identifying the home, Alice took my hand and softly asked if I was glad we had arranged our trip to stop by and visit this little piece of history. From the grin on my face, she knew that I was at a loss for words. For the first time, we both felt the electricity of fully realizing the wonderful friendship that Alice's mother had enjoyed with the daughter of one of America's most iconic couples. Alice wiped away a tear as we walked up the steps.

At a large partner's desk next to the stairs, a well-dressed, middle-aged man sat with a cell phone in one hand and a brochure in the other. He signaled us over, and accepted our $10 admission fee with a warning not to take any flash photos as the original artwork was exposed for viewing. He didn't seem to notice our kitties, and both Munchie and Tuffy seemed content to travel incognito.

I suggested to Alice that we follow the tour outlined in the brochure. On the back cover was an inset photo of Marge's roommate, Scottie Fitzgerald Lanahan, taken sometime in the early '70s before she had left Maryland and returned to Montgomery. It was the first time Alice and I had ever seen a photo of Scottie. Upon her death, Scottie Fitzgerald Lanahan had willed her grandfather's home to the foundation with the stipulation it not be sold but converted into a museum dedicated to preserving both her father, F. Scott's memory, and that of her mother Zelda, as well.

Marge and Scottie had spent two years together as roommates at the University of Colorado when Marge was suddenly stricken with the crippling symptoms of rheumatoid arthritis. Marge had fallen asleep perfectly healthy, but had awakened with flu-like symptoms and was unable to sit up. Scottie had summoned the dorm matron and the chancellor who called for help. Moved immediately to the Memorial Hospital, Marge was soon on a respirator and semiconscious. Only the quick thinking of a young resident saved Marge's life and stalled the progress of a disease that would leave the young sophomore with fingers and joints twisted in pain and deformed. During the following two years, Marge was accompanied by Alice's grandmother on a quest from San Francisco's Angels of Mercy Hospital to the Mayo Clinic in Minnesota to Baltimore's Johns Hopkins Hospital where she was treated by specialists in this debilitating rheumatic disease. Neither shots with gold or stings from bees could slow the inevitable progress of the illness. Only with the discovery of the synthetic corticosteroid prednisone was

231

Marge able to find relief from her painful imprisonment. This relief came with its own price, as it caused the fragile valves in her heart to deteriorate. Scottie and Marge had stayed in touch with each other mostly by phone as Marge's condition had severely restricted her ability to write.

During their roommate years Scottie had always insisted that her father, F. Scott Fitzgerald, was a worn out, alcoholic hack writing news articles in Hollywood, while her mother was a schizophrenic mental patient locked up in an Asheville, North Carolina sanitarium. As their college friendship matured, Marge's roommate shared more of the intimate details of her life with Scott and Zelda. I had read enough about the Roaring '20s famous duo to know there was truth in Scottie's description of her parents' conditions at the time she and Marge had first met.

The Flapper Girl, Zelda, and her great American novelist husband, F. Scott Fitzgerald, had both retreated from the public's imagination as fast as the October, 1929, stock market crash had collapsed the Jazz Age. By the time Scott and Zelda's only child had enrolled in college, the famous couple that had once danced in the fountain at Union Square was back-page news compared with FDR, soup lines, and a monumental land and air war raging in Europe with the very survival of England at stake.

Within a month of their meeting as freshmen students, Scottie gave Marge a first edition of F. Scott Fitzgerald's *Tender is the Night* and said that Marge could learn all there was to know about her parents from that novel. Marge and Scottie were sophomores when Scottie got the message that her, father F. Scott, was dead. A third and fatal heart attack had killed the 44-year old author as he read the newspaper with his paramour in her Laurel Canyon home.

Marge was reading the novel for a second time when her roommate returned from her father's funeral in Maryland. Scottie was distraught, and Marge was saddened to learn that her roommate's mother, Zelda, had remained in the mental hospital, unable to attend her husband's funeral. Zelda had sent a small eight-by-ten-inch unframed, watercolor, self-portrait that she had intended to be placed in F. Scott's coffin and buried with him. Scottie had seen the painting. Surprised to see her mother's signature at the bottom of the haunting portraiture, Scottie held onto the painting and returned with it to show her roommate.

At the time of her father's funeral, Scottie Fitzgerald had had no idea that the Highland Hospital's third-floor hallway in Asheville was lined with watercolors, enamels, and oil paintings signed by the schizophrenic patient named Zelda Sayre Fitzgerald. Two years before the 1948 lethal fire at the Highlands Hospital that killed Zelda and nine other imprisoned women, Scottie Lanahan had taken possession of all her mother's paintings hanging on the walls of the sanitarium. These magical works of art had been lovingly hung in the Cloverdale home when Scottie had finally returned from Maryland to live out her life in Montgomery. Alice's mom had seen these paintings on her visit to Montgomery during the oft-discussed trip to the Mobile casino with her college roommate. Now it was time for Alice, Munchie, Tuffy and me to see and marvel at the originals.

The Leslie and Julian L. McPhillips, Jr., family which was responsible for the museum had done a masterful job of collecting and presenting artifacts belonging to F. Scott and Zelda in a manner that walked the visitor through the couple's storied life. Arranged in separate galleries, the visitor could start in any of the six rooms filled with displays featuring articles, photos and memorabilia related to the Fitzgerald's lives. Alice and I were eager to see Zelda's original artwork displayed in galleries five and six. Alice wanted to start in gallery two and get a glimpse of the archived news articles and photographs immortalizing Zelda's flapper years and the family's experiences in France. After a few minutes of debate over how much time we should devote to anything other than the paintings, Alice convinced me to escort her into each of the six galleries and not rush her. She noticed my wince at this suggestion, which I was convinced might leave us huddled over glass cases reading the fine print from some critic's review of a Fitzgerald novel.

Luckily for me, instead of devoting the museum to meticulously recounting the words and criticisms of F. Scott and Zelda's work, the museum was dedicated to educating interested visitors in the lives and loves of the revered couple. After 90 minutes, I thankfully was no more familiar with Scott Fitzgerald's fictional characters than I had been when we arrived, but I felt a deeper compassion for the couple's despair as the tragic consequences of their actions took control over their destinies.

If Zelda had abided by her father's wishes, she would have never married her author husband and likely avoided the catastrophic emotional and psychological destruction of her own life. If Scott Fitzgerald had chosen soda water over scotch and soda, his alcoholic deliriums would not have restrained his writing legacy to the four slim volumes on display in the Cloverdale museum.

"On the other hand," Alice reminded me, "great inspiration and creativity is frequently born from adversity." She went on to say that she was disappointed that only F. Scott's work was still considered great today whereas Zelda's books, articles and paintings had been nearly forgotten.

Alice had read each of Fitzgerald's novels before entering college. She had enjoyed Fitzgerald's expressive style requiring nine full pages of fluid paragraphs of multisyllabic adjectives to convince the reader that Anthony Patch in *The Beautiful and The Damned* was not the artist's fictional character. My introduction to Fitzgerald came in consort with a freshman required-reading list that included the big three: Salinger, Vonnegut and Fitzgerald. My passion for history, biographies and memoirs left me unenthused with each of the authors, with the least interest of all in Fitzgerald.

Compared to Fitzgerald's nine pages to prove reality of Anthony Patch I preferred David Copperfield's simple proof of his character's non-fictional existence with three words: "I was born," or Melville's equally pithy, "Call me Ishmael." When it came to using the weather to set the scene, Fitzgerald inked up half a page with descriptive language setting the mood for Gatsby to tell Nick that Daisy never loved Tom. Compare this to Edward Bulwer-Lytton's, "It was a dark and stormy night" that got the job done in seven words. Though it is, perhaps, the most hackneyed words in the English language, those seven words to me were more effective than F. Scott's one-hundred-and-fifty.

In the next gallery, I learned that F. Scott Fitzgerald had not completed his college education. Led to believe, since my college days, that the author's fascination with the rich and privileged he had encountered at Princeton had influenced his writing, I was shocked to discover he hadn't even finished his first year. He had, in fact, dropped out and enlisted in the army as a soldier in the Great War when he was assigned to Fort Sheridan in Montgomery, Alabama. That was where he met Zelda at a party.

We proceeded with growing anticipation to see the Zelda originals. Alice noticed the smug look on my face when I gave a thumbs-up at the news article in the gallery that linked Zelda to one of our favorite songs by the *Eagles*. We had both seen the article years ago when it was first published. Don Henley had confirmed that he and Bernie Leadon had been inspired by Zelda's legend and written *Witchy Woman* as a tribute to her heroic style. The first time Alice and I listened to this song together, I had told her she reminded me of the song because no one pushed harder or flew higher than my Rockette girl. For our 10th wedding anniversary, I bought front-row concert tickets at the D.C. Convention Center to see Don Henley and the *Eagles*. I had sent a fax to the band manager encouraging the band to include the haunting tune, *Witchy Woman*, in the night's

235

playlist. They did. Twenty-five years later, on our last trip to Ireland, we had again had front-row tickets to the *History of the Eagles Tour* at the O2 arena in Dublin. Once again, I submitted the same request. As the second set opened, Glenn Frey strummed the first chords and whispered in the mic, "This one's for Alice," and my Rockette girl beamed as the music flowed with:

"She's a restless spirit on an endless flight
woo hooo witchy woman
see how high she flies"

Alice shushed my singing of the tune as we strolled into the two rooms of the museum. Zelda's remains may rest in the Catholic cemetery in Maryland, but her spirit lives in an old Southern manse on a quiet residential street in Montgomery, Alabama. It was in the last gallery rooms that we finally saw the real *Three Little Pigs* and my favorite Zelda painting, the *Smoky Mountains* landscape. It was inconspicuously displayed on a side wall. If only Alice's Mom could have been alive and traveling with us to visit these rooms and see her roommate's paintings one last time, but I was happy that she had visited when the house was still inhabited by the very vibrant Scottie.

Alice Tells All

As we pulled away from the Zayre house in Montgomery, Alice, continued to flip through the photos she held on her lap. As we continued our drive to Atlanta Alice entertained me by describing each of the photos and what she thought Zelda may have been thinking when she painted the originals. We had not discussed more than half the lot when our GPS announced the exit to Buckhead was just ahead. Never had we seen our two little guys so excited to discover a new room as we did when we unzipped their carriers in the

4th-floor suite at the Buckhead Grand Hyatt. We would spend two glorious nights enveloped by thick, beige carpet; and a luxurious bath with marble vanity and Moen double-showerhead fixtures set in a porcelain Jacuzzi tub. As much as we enjoyed the grandeur of the majestic Monteleone Hotel in New Orleans, there was something to be said for immaculate modern. With ten-foot high ceilings and floor-to-ceiling windows sucking in the bright Atlanta afternoon sunshine, we expected to look outside and see an azure sea with waves breaking on a white sandy beach. What we saw instead was equally amazing.

Our building was one of a dozen skyscrapers with squared-off glass and chrome corners jutting out of a cluster of multi-story shopping malls, restaurants and office buildings. High-rise hotels were jammed together in an oasis of New Atlanta called Buckhead. Outside the metroplex of glass and steel, the traffic-jammed roads of Peachtree Street, Peachtree Avenue, and Peachtree Road snaked under 100-year-old sycamores, past brick and stucco mansions and into the South's most vibrant economic juggernaut – the city of Atlanta. Home to Coca Cola, the Atlanta Braves, and the world's largest saltwater aquarium, the city prided itself on preserving its history while encouraging progress at any price. Its overflowing, business-friendly community extended into internationally known residential zones and generated edge-cities around Marietta, Roswell, Sandy Springs and, of course, Buckhead.

Anyone intending to sample the hottest-trending food spots in America would have to visit Atlanta. Buckhead is at the very epicenter of everything that made New Atlanta the Berlin of America. If Potsdamerplatz was the beating heart of the new German capital, then Buckhead was the Cullinan Diamond of the Atlanta crown jewels. Rising from the dark earth and lush greenery of the Georgia countryside, the Buckhead Metroplex is a 21st-century oasis of edgy architecture housing the latest and greatest in high-technology ventures, medical arts and residential exuberance.

Like moths to flames, food chefs were drawn to the empires of well-heeled, salarymen and women, not to mention entrepreneurs. With them came a competitive spirit that fueled a food culture that outranked Manhattan in both scope and quality. Atlanta's culinary dominance is debated only among those who have never actually visited the Buckhead area for themselves.

Alice and I had Niko Bistro and Aria on our list. In less than five minutes, we could walk down Peachtree Road and into the front door of Niko Bistro. For our Aria visit, we needed Uber.

Tonight was Aria's night. We were unsure about taking the kitties. They would not have minded remaining in their new playroom at the Grand Hyatt. Munchie was rolling on her back inside the floor-length window, and Tuffy was in the middle of the king-size bed, prowling back and forth from one end of the mattress to the other with an occasional side-trip to climb onto the oversized pillows. One look at them so content with their situation and Alice christened them Buckhead Cats. The name stuck with me, and I have continued to refer to them as our Buckheads. We decided to take the Buckheads with us to Aria. They would be in their carriers, so what could possibly go wrong?

We stood side-by-side, my arm around Alice's waist, transfixed on the Buckhead view from our spacious room in the Grand Hyatt. Curious to know if Alice was comfortable with me in the capital of the New South, I asked her if she still loved me. She pulled me close and fixed me with a look that said 'Concentrate and pay attention.' Each word she spoke pumped more blood into my heart that was already swelling with enough to nearly force me to clutch my chest. "I have loved you with all my soul since the moment you said. 'It doesn't matter.'"

I remembered saying those words. I had said them twice to Alice as we sat one Saturday night in the green leather booth at the bar side of RT's Cajun restaurant. It had been three months since Alice and the kitties had moved from her small Dupont Circle apartment into my more spacious abode after saying no to my marriage proposal at Mr. K's. The ring with my mother's diamond was in the tiny, felt-lined ring box, and the box was in full view on the window shelf in the kitchen. I put it there so Alice could see it every day and put it on her finger if she ever agreed to marry me. For three months, Alice left each day in her British racing-green MGB and usually dropped me at the nearest Metro stop for my trip to the office. Our schedules rarely allowed a shared ride home.

On weekends, we would explore the many eclectic tastes of the D.C. food scene. On most weeknights, I dropped by a variety of takeout places to garner our dinner. When Alice's key rattled in the lock, LeRoy and Evie Mae would both bound off their pillows or jump out of their cardboard boxes and head for the front door. That was my cue to set the table, pull the takeout from the microwave, and pour the tea. After a few minutes, Alice would simply step into the kitchen and perform a tiny curtsy, as though I were sitting on a throne instead of in a high-back kitchen chair. LeRoy and Evie Mae were right behind her. They hopped onto the table, curled their legs under their bellies and assumed the watchful profile of the Egyptian Sphinx. Directly behind me and slightly above my head was the window shelf holding the ring box. Every night, I kept watch to see if Alice would look up to see if the box was still there. She didn't say anything, but every night I eventually spied her taking a quick glance.

Alice worked late in her job and had extracurricular activities like her Jazzercise classes. What she did not have was weekend work. Alice's firm maintained a strict no-weekend-work policy in recognition of the long work days and the extended periods of travel that invariably accompanied the projects. My company's employee rolls were filled with unmarried young computer geeks, software wizards, financial planners and business analysts who never missed the company's Saturday buffet lunches. Business proposals written on most Saturdays came with a free lunch and the chance to socialize and maybe find a date for that night. I had spent the past two Saturdays working on proposals, and Alice wanted to know my plans for the weekend. I knew that the following Saturday would be a short day, so I invited Alice to pick me up at noon at my office. I suggested going to Georgetown for lunch and staying for the music down at the waterfront park. Alice suggested we end the day at RT's.

The first days of fall usually ushered in cooler days and much lower humidity, and that Saturday began and ended with perfect weather for Washington, D.C. The high that day would be in the mid-80s, so I wasn't surprised when Alice pulled up to the curb with the top down on the MGB. She offered me that radiant smile with her shiny red lipstick and emerald-green eyes flashing under her freshly trimmed, sun-streaked, bangs. I stretched my leg over the low door and slid into the bucket seat next to my Rockette girl. Alice passed me the Walkman as she shifted into first and headed for Key Bridge and Georgetown.

M Street neatly divides Georgetown into upper and lower sections. Running perpendicular and cutting across M Street are all the numbered side streets from 28th to 37th. The upper section of Georgetown flows gradually uphill until it reaches the National Cathedral on Wisconsin Avenue. The lower section falls away steeply downhill. Along the riverfront stands the Kennedy Center that adjoins a line of restaurants, bars and outdoor theater venues that extend almost to the Key Bridge on 37th Street.

Tourists on foot clog the sidewalks and paths on the Mall. Tourists in cars clog the side streets in Georgetown. On the Mall, tourists stop to admire the old, brick Smithsonian building and other historical sights. The hundreds of people streaming behind these oblivious tourists simply step around them and continue on. But, when cars stop on the Georgetown streets to admire the canal, other cars can't scoot around like the pedestrians do on the Mall. Alice was turning off M Street into 31st and was heading downhill when a man with Empire State-tags decided to stop while going uphill on 31st to admire the historic mule-drawn barges at the C&O canal crossing. As our cars passed each other with Alice clutching and downshifting to slow down the MGB, the man in the Empire State-tagged car was being deafened by the horn blasts from the angry multitude trapped behind him in their overheating autos. We passed within inches of his stopped car, and I tipped a friendly salute at the open passenger window, smiling at his predicament with a knowing grin. Alice threw a quick glance my way and immediately downshifted and pressed on the gas, flinging us downhill toward Water Street which borders the Potomac.

My Walkman earphones sealed off the car horn blasts, but Alice's race downhill caught my attention. I pulled off the headphones just as she slowed down to make a right turn at the bottom of the hill. She said she wanted to get out of the traffic and away from the angry horns.

"Fine by me." I restored the headphones and fast-forwarded to the Stones' *Get Off of My Cloud.*

Alice made another quick, right turn going up 30th Street in the opposite direction from which we had just come. Suddenly, it wasn't clear to me where we were heading. Alice kept adjusting the rear-view mirror on the MGB as she downshifted, stepped on the gas, and drove uphill toward the stop sign on M and 30th Streets. An excellent driver, she brought the MGB to a complete stop at the top of 30th Street at M Street. We were tilted back at a modest angle on the steep hill, and Alice looked worried as she scanned the M Street traffic looking for a chance to shift, brake, clutch, and gas into traffic. A space opened up in the traffic, and as Alice clutched with her left foot and moved her right foot from the brake to the gas, the MGB rolled backwards and gently tapped the front bumper of the car behind us. I looked back to see the Empire State tags.

Alice popped the clutch and hit the gas, propelling us into the M Street traffic. The driver of the Empire State-tagged auto was hanging out the window, swinging his fist above his head and yelling something indecipherable. As Alice sped down M Street toward Key Bridge, I turned around and could just make out the car turning onto M Street to follow us. Alice was staring in the rear-view mirror when I asked what she was worried about. She had insurance on the car, and the bumper tap could not possibly have done any damage. Alice said she was worried that the driver might call the police, and she didn't want any points on her license.

"In that case," I suggested, "why don't we make a sharp turn up Wisconsin, cut back through Upper Georgetown, and head onto the Rock Creek Parkway?" No tourist would be able to keep up with us on that route. We could scoot back to my office and park in the garage.

Alice said, "Good idea," and made the turn.

Security opened and closed the doors on our offices on weekends. Our key-cards were for ID, only, on weekends, and the inside-garage entrance is locked, requiring a short walk out and up to the front glass doors of the building. Alice was hanging onto my arm as I tugged her up the steps to the door. She was shaking her head, seemingly bothered by our minor scrape with the tourist and our subsequent sneaky run back to my office. I told her to forget about it as I pushed the call button for the security guard sitting at the desk inside the glass foyer. But as I glanced at the street, I spied the Empire State-tags on a maroon sedan edging up to the curb in front.

"Oh, no." I laughed. I gestured to Alice to turn around. The driver was on foot, pointing his finger at us, and hollering something like, "Mister, I need to see you."

Alice grabbed my arm in a strong squeeze and said, "Let's get inside before he gets here."

"I need to see you," he shouted again, bounding up the stairs. He was close to my height but outweighed me by twenty or 30 pounds. His hair was trimmed with neat, military whitewalls.

Deciding that caution was the better part of valor, I followed Alice's advice and said, "Buddy, you are a danger to society, and the security guard can deal with you."

At the mention of security, the man saw the guard walking down the tiled hallway to open the door. Alice hit the call button again to urge the guard to speed it up. The Empire State-driver turned, and in two leaps bounded back down the stairs, and shouted over his shoulder, "This isn't over." He slipped behind the wheel and drove off.

By the time the elevator took us up to my office on the tenth floor, Alice appeared to have shaken off the scare. We sat down, and I once again tried to calm her. I told her that we shouldn't let our weekend be ruined due to some overreacting tourist who would feel as stupid as he deserved to by tomorrow. I reminded Alice it was a nothing accident, and he was as much at fault as she, but I gave the guy credit for managing to follow our circuitous route back to my office. If he really wanted to report the accident, he could trace the tag of Alice's car and turn it over to his insurance company.

My words seemed to be working, and Alice agreed we shouldn't let the encounter interfere with our weekend. Our dinner reservations were for 6:00 p.m. at RT's, and we compromised on how to spend the rest of the afternoon. Alice wanted to drive over to the vet's office before it closed to pick up more Frontline for the kitties. I decided to check on my company's proposal writers, lend a hand in assembling the response and making copies for our prospect. Alice agreed to pick me up at the office at 5:30 p.m. and we would head out for dinner.

Alice was fifteen minutes late, and I was standing on the curb listening to a new artist with the unpronounceable name of Englebert Humperdinck on the Walkman. The MGB pulled up with the top up, and I had to bend down and open the door to slide in. I had jettisoned the ring box in my desk and slipped the engagement ring into my pants pocket, wrapped in a napkin.

Alice had been crying. She shook her head, and said she would tell me all about it at the restaurant. We drove in silence. Neither of us said a word until we opened the door to RT's and headed for our cherished booth in the back. Alice was still dabbing away at her eyes when Lynn sat our two flutes of Bouchard white bourgogne on the table. Under even the most stressful situations, I had observed Alice to be calm. She did not typically overreact, so I was mystified by her apparent distress.

"Was it the accident?" I said.

"No, it was the driver." she answered.

"Did he come after you? Did you see him after you left the office?" I asked.

"No," she said, "but I must tell you about him."

I wondered what there was to tell.

"He's my husband," she said."He's what?" I coughed out. "He's what?" It was all I could say. "His name is Barry, and I'm still married to him."

In some cool place behind my eyes, a feeling of helplessness began to grow. My arms fell by my sides as though they were no longer attached to my shoulders. I felt saliva pooling on my tongue, but I couldn't swallow. My breath stopped, and I couldn't feel my chest.

Alice leaned across the booth, took my face in her hands but I couldn't feel her touch. She pressed her thumbs against my cheeks, but I couldn't feel them, either. My fingertips burned. My eyes shut. I was cold. Alice later told me that my face was white as chalk.

"Open your eyes," she whispered loudly. The intensity of her demand flicked my eyelids open to her glossy red lips, and mascara-stained tears spilling on to the table.

"Talk to me. Say something," she demanded, not caring if anyone was watching.

From inside my chest, a deep breath took hold, and as the air rushed out, I hoarsely whispered the only words that could possibly save me. "Are you still my Rockette girl?"

"Yes," she said. "Yes, I am still your Rockette girl but I am married. Do you hear me?"

"Yes." I heard her. "It doesn't matter. It doesn't matter," was all I could say

Alice had married Barry the day he graduated from the U.S. Air Force Academy as a Second Lieutenant. They had met the previous year when Alice attended a Denver Christmas ball celebrating the Academy cadets. Alice discovered too late that she had fallen in love with the uniform and had impulsively said yes to Barry's proposal after having been out with the Catholic-reared Iowa farm boy only four times, and always in the presence of friends.

Upon his graduation, his first assignment was to an upstate New York Air Force support unit only a short drive from where Alice had been admitted to grad school. The newly-weds had easily secured a large five-figure loan immediately upon Barry's graduation from the Air Force Academy. It had been intended for Alice's tuition expenses and to purchase the furnishings for their new apartment. Barry had splurged on the very best Japanese and German high-fidelity music equipment, including a Marantz 6370Q turntable and an expensive pair of Kloss Advent speakers. He had spent almost $1000 filling a small wine cabinet with French cabernets and Sonoma Cutrer chardonnays. He fed his gadget addiction with a Walkman fix and ordered the best Leica camera accessories from an overseas catalogue. Barry had paid cash for an MGB and passed it over to Alice to use in her daily commute. Alice could not have been happier

245

with their good fortune until the third month of their marriage. Alice left her classes early to return to the apartment to prepare a surprise 90-day wedding anniversary for her handsome Air Force husband. Instead of an empty apartment, she opened the front door and heard sounds in the bedroom. Barry and his young female supply sergeant were amorously entangled, and oblivious to Alice standing in the hallway, dumbstruck with shame and panic. Alice backed out without making a sound. Instead she made plans for complete dissolution and separation. She waited two weeks until Barry walked out of the apartment with his overnight bag, packed for a trip to Elmendorf Air Base for a three-day recertification course. Alice alerted the local moving company and before night fall everything in the apartment except for the mattress had been safely spirited away with Three Guys and a Truck on its way to Alice's new apartment in Ithaca where it would remain until Alice finished her grad studies. Barry returned from his trip to discover he was left with his signature on a large bank note and an empty house.

Three years after these events occurred I came across these communal possessions in a sixth floor P Street apartment on Dupont Circle the night I met Alice's babies LeRoy and Evie Mae. Alice was comfortably ensconced in her place in the Finger Lakes by the time Barry recovered from the shock of his new bride's sudden abandonment. He knew he had been measured and found wanting. At first, he thought the punishment didn't fit the crime. Losing his new bride due to a summer fling was bad enough, but to lose all his personal effects and being held liable for a bank loan that was financing his spurned wife's MBA degree while she tooled around in a new MGB pushed him to the limit. He had made contact once, only to be told by my Rockette girl that he could drop dead, and if he didn't like what had happened, he could sue her. That had been the last Alice had heard of Barry for three years – until this week when he had come to Washington D.C. looking for her.

After three years of flying the world in an Air Force tanker, another young, impressionable female college graduate had fallen for the uniform, and Barry wanted to marry her. He couldn't. He and his fiancé were Catholic. In order to marry in the Catholic Church Barry needed an annulment from his marriage to Alice.

"It doesn't matter?" Alice cried. "What do you mean 'it doesn't matter?' I'm married," she repeated. "To a man I haven't seen in over three years."

"It doesn't matter," I said, slowly coming back to my senses, "because I am completely and desperately in love with you, and nothing else matters. You are my Rockette girl, and I will always love you. What you've written on my heart is all that matters, not what is written on a piece of paper. I don't want to lose you."

Now I understood why she had refused my proposal and my ring. In addition to being married, she didn't want to risk another marriage and have the same thing happen again. She had to be sure I would love her and not betray her. Alice told me she had taken the transfer from her New York office to D.C. in order to obtain a no-fault divorce under the District's more liberal statutes. This process was already underway, and she had planned to share her past with me when Barry suddenly appeared on the scene.

She looked at me and softly spoke. "You really and truly do love me with all your being don't you, Pat?"

"Yes! Yes!" I said. I reached into my pocket and pulled out the napkin with the ring wrapped tightly inside. I slipped the ring on her finger. And this time Alice said, "YES!"

That night at RT's was not an ordinary dinner but a celebration of Alice finally agreeing to marry me. Yes, there was still the obstacle of getting her marriage annulled, but even if I didn't know how to deal with it, I knew that I would not accept failure in this task. Nothing would keep me from spending the rest of my life with this girl who loved cats, my

Rockette. Now, 35 years later, we were still exploring life together and living our promise till death us do part as we continue "Dining and Driving with Cats."

The adventure isn't over. Join us for more "Dining and Driving with Cats" in the sequel "Dining and Driving with Cats 2 – Alice Rising". Coming soon.

If you enjoyed this story please stop by Amazon Kindle and give a review – your kind words will make a difference,

All the best,
Pat and Alice and the cats